difficult for m **off you, you** **added, in tha****t**** ****kind of male growl**** guaranteed to set her nerves fluttering expectantly.**

He walked towards Shelby slowly. 'I'm going to have my work cut out keeping my mind on my job tonight.'

She was pleased she had achieved her first objective and knocked him off balance this way. Of course she hadn't meant to get knocked off balance herself in the process! 'I thought I was your job, and your plan was to keep an eye on me,' she reminded him, her breath hitching in her throat as he stopped mere inches away. 'Seems like you have a problem, Gray. Let me solve it for you. Take the evening off. I promise not to tell,' she added in a confidential whisper.

Amanda Browning still lives in the Essex house where she was born. The third of four children—her sister being her twin—she enjoyed the rough and tumble of life with two brothers as much as she did reading books. Writing came naturally as an outlet for a fertile imagination. The love of books led her to a career in libraries, and being single allowed her to take the leap into writing for a living. Success is still something of a wonder, but allows her to indulge in hobbies as varied as embroidery and bird-watching.

Recent titles by the same author:

THE LAWYER'S CONTRACT MARRIAGE

HER TYCOON PROTECTOR

BY
AMANDA BROWNING

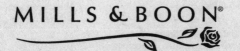
MILLS & BOON®

First published in Great Britain 2005
Paperback Edition 2006
Harlequin Mills & Boon Limited,
Eton House, 18-24 Paradise Road, Richmond, Surrey TW9 1SR

© Amanda Browning 2005

ISBN 0 263 84790 X

Set in Times Roman 10½ on 11½ pt.
01-0206-54576

Printed and bound in Spain
by Litografia Rosés, S.A., Barcelona

CHAPTER ONE

SHELBY GREER paced angrily across the carpet. She looked wildly dramatic in her electric-blue suit, with her shoulder-length auburn hair bouncing at every long-legged stride. She had been blessed with a classically oval face and fine features that would be considered beautiful by any standards, but right now her ice-green eyes, with their thick long lashes, were flashing sparks. She was fuming. A volatile volcano just waiting to explode. Abruptly she turned to face the man who stood before the elegant Adam fireplace.

'No! Absolutely not! There's no way I'm going to have my world turned upside down—not in a million years. I'm not giving up my independence on the basis of a threat that might not be real,' she declared vehemently in response to his proposal.

'Now, Shelby, be reasonable,' her father pleaded with her. 'If you won't come and stay here where I can look after you, then you have to have a bodyguard.'

'No, I most certainly do not!' Shelby disagreed instantly. 'I'm perfectly capable of looking after myself. If you think for one second that I would allow a complete stranger to enter my home and invade my privacy, you're crazy.' The mere thought of it made her shudder with distaste.

'If it's crazy to care what happens to you, then I'm guilty as charged,' her father shot back. 'Threats have been made against you, Shelby. I have to take them seriously. Why won't you?'

'Because it's all so utterly ridiculous! The man's a crank, out for what he can get. Why should I allow him to upset

5

my life? No, I'm sorry, Dad, but to keep trying to change my mind is a complete and utter waste of time,' she declared adamantly, though she secretly admitted to a few butterflies in her stomach when he had first told her. 'Trust me on this. Nothing is going to happen.'

'So you keep telling me,' Oscar Greer responded calmly to his only daughter's outburst. He had, after all, known what to expect. She was headstrong and independent and, on occasions such as these, over-confident that she knew best.

Shelby flung up her hands despairingly. 'Then why aren't you listening to me?' She loved her father dearly, and knew he had only her best interests at heart, but this was going too far. 'I don't need a nursemaid, Dad!'

'I'm glad to hear it,' her father returned dryly. 'At twenty-eight, you should be able to wash, dress and feed yourself.'

That piece of whimsy earned him another exasperated look. 'You know what I mean. This is so unnecessary.'

'Really? I had no idea you could look into the future?'

Shelby turned away in frustration. There was no getting through to him. He wasn't going to budge an inch. There were times when she could twist him round her little finger, but this was not one of them. He loved her, but he would only twist when he wanted to. This time he intended to have his way. Well, she was as determined as he was. She was not about to give in this time.

Sighing heavily, she walked to the window and looked out at the rain-lashed gardens of her father's Hampstead home. She had grown up here, an only child but never a lonely one. Her father was London's most successful media magnate, but he had always had time for his daughter. The bond was a close one. He needed her compliance for his own peace of mind. Normally she would gladly have given it to him, but this was different. She couldn't alter her life because of a threat she didn't believe existed, however much she loved her father. All she could try to do was make him see things from her point of view.

'Let's go over it again. What exactly did the message say?' she asked in a more reasonable tone as she turned to her parent.

Oscar Greer's expression became grim. 'The gist of it was that one of our papers had printed something this individual didn't like, and he intended to take some form of revenge. He used the phrase, 'The sins of the father shall pass down to the daughter.' Which the police consider a direct threat to you. Which is why you are going to have a bodyguard, like it or not. You're all I have and I'm not prepared to risk losing you.'

That, of course, tweaked her heartstrings, and with a faint groan she hurried over to give him a hug. 'You aren't going to lose me,' she reassured him fiercely. 'But I'm still not going to have a bodyguard!' she added hastily, so he wouldn't think she had given in.

Her father grimaced as he hugged her back. 'My God, but you're stubborn. The police wanted to lock you away somewhere safe for the duration, but I knew I'd never get you to agree to that either!' he told her as he released her.

Shelby's lips curved in an unseen smile of relief as she crossed to the tray of drinks on the antique sideboard, helping herself to a small brandy. She needed it, for she had never had to fight so strongly with her father before. It wasn't comfortable. Now that she had won, she began to relax.

'You were right about that. I have commitments. I can't just up sticks and disappear.'

She was that most fashion conscious of modern individuals—an interior designer. Her mother had been an artist, and it was from her that Shelby had inherited her eye for colour and texture. After a false start, she had studied art and design at college and then had gone on to start her own business. There had been small jobs to begin with, but word of mouth had soon spread about the quality of her work. One thing had led to another, until now she was so busy she had taken on a small staff of helpers. She was fully aware that there were people who thought that, as her father's heir, she led a cushioned existence and only played at her work. They were wrong. Her business was her own baby from start to finish and she took it very seriously indeed. Her books were full and she even had a waiting list.

With a wry shake of her head, she curled up in a corner of the couch. 'Lord, I can't believe you actually expected me to agree to have a minder!' Funnily enough, she had been told once that she needed a minder, but she shied away from the memory. It had been totally embarrassing for her. He, of course, had found it vastly amusing. 'You've had threats before. Why are you taking this one so seriously?'

'I prefer not to take chances with your life, my girl,' Oscar pronounced, glancing at his watch, then checking that against the mantel clock. Rocking back on his heels, he slipped his hand into his jacket pocket and studied his polished shoes.

'Are you expecting someone?' she asked, fascinated by these unexpected signs of unease in him.

He cleared his throat. 'Since you ask, the chap I've arranged to watch your back is arriving tonight.'

Shelby's eyes widened in shock. 'You already arranged it? Before asking me?' So much for winning! She should have guessed he would do something like this.

'I knew you wouldn't agree, so I made the decision for you,' her father confirmed with a nod of his head. 'I decided the best option was to present you with a *fait accompli*.'

She was on her feet in an instant. 'You had no right to do that, Dad. I know you're concerned, but this is my life we're talking about. Well, I hope you and he have an enjoyable evening, because you'll be spending it without me. I'm leaving!' She moved to make good her threat, but had only taken one short step towards her handbag when her father spoke.

'Stay right where you are, Shelby. You're going nowhere,' he commanded in a voice she hadn't heard in years. It brought her up short, blinking in surprise.

'You can't force me to have a bodyguard!' she protested in disbelief, which made Oscar Greer smile grimly.

'I can, and I am.'

'This is absurd!' Shelby exclaimed, but she sat down again just as the front doorbell rang loudly. She twisted round so she could watch the lounge door from over the back of the couch. 'Is this him? Well, I don't care how nice he is; I'm not going to have anything to do with him,' she added for good measure, listening to the housekeeper opening the front door, and the sound of voices joined in friendly conversation. Then footsteps headed towards the closed door and she held her breath.

The man who entered was in his mid-thirties, black-haired, blue-eyed and handsome as sin. Wearing a brown leather bomber jacket over blue shirt and jeans, he was indeed the sexiest thing on two legs she had seen in many a long day. Broad-shouldered to boot. He was tall and had the sort of long legs and lean hips that she found particularly attractive. He also had the kind of chest a girl could snuggle up on and drift into dreams that would make an angel blush. She didn't have to ask if he was also charming and witty. She knew. He was, after all, Gray Compton, her father's troubleshooter and the man she had been in love with for simply aeons.

For one intense moment Shelby's world stood still. Lord,

but her heart was pleased to see him. Life had been a desert since the last time they had met. Not that he would know it, she reminded herself as time ticked on again. She had her pride, after all.

They had been friends once, when she was younger. He had been the closest thing to a brother she would ever have. They had teased and taunted each other, much as all brothers and sisters did, and it might have stayed that way if fate had not intervened. Quite out of the blue, and when she had least expected it, she had fallen in love with him. Naturally, having done something so rash, and knowing he still only saw her as a sister, she had had to camouflage her feelings for her own protection.

She had often teased Gray about the women in his life, but had found herself in the unenviable position of wanting to be one. The only one. To her despair, he had never seen her that way. Jealousy had raised its ugly head. To combat it she had taken to dating like it was going out of fashion, though rarely dating the same man for long, to hide the fact there was only one man she really wanted. For his part, Gray had observed her behaviour with undisguised amusement.

Their relationship had stayed pretty much the same, although he had now started teasing her about the men in her life too. She had hidden her unhappiness well and, save for one minor blip when she had succumbed to a moment of recklessness, she had lived with the situation. So it might have gone on, but then something had happened which had made her hate him. She couldn't forget it, nor forgive it, no matter how much she loved him—and, for her sins, she did still love him.

So now, whenever they met, they engaged in a constant war of words. It was the perfect shield, and Shelby doubted if anyone but herself knew how she really felt. Right now, though, she wished she had had some warning he was coming to dinner tonight, in order to get her defences in place.

Gray Compton allowed his gaze to meet that of a bemused Shelby. 'Hi, there, Red. Long time no see.'

Shelby winced at the nickname she had been given as a child because of her hair. Of course, Gray would insist on using it still, just to irritate her. She smiled thinly. 'Well, well, if it isn't Dad's blue-eyed boy. What are you doing here, Gray? Coming to see what trouble you can cause?'

For once he didn't come back with a mocking rejoinder. 'My job, sweetheart. Just my job,' he told her briefly, making her frown.

Having grown used to their bickering over recent years, Oscar Greer ignored it and crossed the room, hand held out. 'Gray, my boy. Thank you for coming.'

The younger man smiled warmly and shook his hand. 'You knew I would, Oscar.' He had been sorting out a problem in Japan when he had received Oscar's call for help. 'I jumped on the first plane out.'

'How was the trip?'

'Tiring, but I'm used to it.'

Light dawned for Shelby, and her heart sank. Her eyes hastily sought her father's, hoping to have her fears allayed. 'Dad, please tell me this isn't the man you've roped in to look after me!' she pleaded in horror, more appalled than she could ever reveal. If there was one person she didn't want to spend any intimate time with, Gray was that man. Mostly because the only person she wanted was the self-same man!

Gray walked further into the room, his expression one of grim amusement at her response. 'I didn't think you'd be thrilled, but think about it, Red. Who else would be doing a spot of troubleshooting for the boss?'

Their eyes locked. The challenge given and received. Both understood the message. Whether the work was clean or dirty, Gray was the man for the job. Especially where she was concerned.

'When it comes to sorting out trouble, you are the best in the business, Gray,' her father complimented, seemingly unaware of the undercurrents swirling around the room. 'I would willingly pay you double your salary for what you're doing for us.'

The younger man shook his head. 'You know that's not necessary, Oscar. I'm only too happy to help you and my old sparring partner, Red, here. In fact, I wouldn't want it any other way.'

Oh, she knew how he threw himself into his work all right, Shelby acknowledged bitterly. She swung her feet to the floor and stood up for a second time. 'OK, that's it. I'm not having him. If I wanted anyone, which I don't, I most certainly wouldn't have him. He'll make my life a misery.' She refused point-blank, earning herself a mocking look from Gray for her pains.

'Then you'll just have to be miserable,' her father declared sternly. 'I chose Gray to be your bodyguard, so let that be an end to it. Now, can I get you something to drink, Gray? Whisky was always your favourite tipple.'

'Better make it a small one, with plenty of water. I'm driving.'

'But, Dad!' Shelby tried to protest as he crossed to the other side of the room, only to find he wasn't listening. 'What did I do to deserve this?' she muttered, then caught Gray's eye and the mockery there. 'Don't say a word!'

'And you looked so grown up too,' he derided with a shake of his head. 'Now I get closer I can see you're still the same old Shelby, always thinking more about yourself than anyone else.'

She was outraged at the claim. 'How can you say that?'

'Easily. I grew up with you, remember. You always brought your trials and tribulations to your father. I lost

count of the number of times I was there when you came
to bemoan the fate of your latest romance,' he responded
sardonically, reminding her of hazy summer days when life
was simpler, before she had fallen in love with him and
discovered she would have to keep it a secret from everyone for the sake of her pride and her heart.

'Where else was I supposed to go? I never had a mother
to confide in,' Shelby reminded him. Her mother had died
when she was little more than a baby, leaving her father to
take on both roles, which he had done magnificently so far
as she was concerned.

'Hmm, your mother might have altered your dating habits. Has anyone told you that you go through men like a
hot knife through butter?' he asked her, and she sent him
a scathing look.

'You're a fine one to talk. Watching the turnover of
women in your life makes me dizzy!' she returned swiftly,
knowing that the difference between them was that she
dated to hide the fact her heart was already hooked. As
smokescreens went, it was pretty damn good. He never saw
through it, and that was the whole point of the exercise.

'You can't think so badly of me when you're attracted
to me yourself. Let's not forget you even made a play for
me once.'

Her heart twisted at the painful reminder, but she managed to hide behind a curl of her lip. 'Yes, well, I was less
discriminating when I was young.' She had been twenty
and heartsick and, bolstered by liquid courage, she had
made her only attempt to seduce him. Her failure had
bruised her pride, but her feelings hadn't changed. Then,
of course, there was that other time... 'Your actions later
had nothing so reasonable to commend them. Merely a
slavish devotion to duty,' she returned scornfully.

A nerve ticked in Gray's jaw as he shook his head wryly.

'You certainly know how to hold a grudge, don't you, Red?'

Shelby smiled at him frostily. 'Did you think I wouldn't? You were a first-class rat, and that's the way I shall always think of you,' she hissed back. Oh, what a whopper of a lie that was.

'All because I did nothing?'

'It isn't what you did or didn't do, it was why you did it. My God, you made me think you wanted me, when all you were doing was following orders. It was crass and unworthy of you, Gray. How could you have stooped so low, even for my father? Don't expect me to ever forgive you.' Shelby declared bitingly, her green eyes icy with scorn.

Gray's eyes glittered. 'You know, Red, you have to be one of the few redheads I know who actually live up to their billing. Makes a man wonder.'

It was a leading remark, and she knew she shouldn't go there, but she just couldn't help herself. It was always like that with Gray.

'Makes you wonder what?' she asked, and his wicked grin was fair warning that she wouldn't like what he was about to say.

'If you're as passionate in bed as out of it,' Gray responded, with the kind of glint in his eye that made her heart turn over.

She looked at him haughtily. 'Too late. You had your chance and you blew it. Trust me, Gray, that is the one thing you will never, ever find out now.' As she would never find out what it would be like to be made love to by him. But that was a mental path better not travelled.

He tutted. 'You're just put out because I discovered you were attracted to me,' he riposted, taking her breath away at his gall.

Sadly, she couldn't deny it. She had given herself away in the unexpected joy of what she had believed the moment was. 'All that does is make me human, even if my taste is doubtful. What does it say of you, when you merely pretended to want me?' she countered thickly.

'Who said it was all pretence? You're an attractive woman, despite your faults,' Gray argued, momentarily knocking Shelby off balance, but she rallied swiftly.

'*I* do. I was there, remember? You turned the heat on and off as easily as flicking a switch! It was disgusting. You didn't want me. You were just doing your job. I hope your conscience doesn't let you sleep nights.'

Something flickered in and out of his eyes before she could catch it, and his jaw set. 'If my conscience bothers me, it wouldn't be because of you. Anyway, I'm curious. What irks you more, Red? That I might have pretended to want you, or that I stopped before things went too far?'

Oh, that took the biscuit. She felt like scratching his eyes out. 'You have no idea how glad I am you stopped. I would never have felt clean again if you hadn't. No wonder my father likes you so much. Your commitment to your work is unparalleled. But I don't like you, and if you imagine for one second I'm going to sit still for this—' she began, only to end on a gasp as his hand snaked out and fastened on her wrist.

Gray's lips remained curved in a smile in case Oscar should turn and see them, but his eyes were coldly angry. 'Listen to me, you're going to do exactly what's expected of you. I have a great deal of respect and affection for your father, and I won't have you worrying him so much he ends up in hospital. For some reason that escapes me, he loves you, and if you have any feelings for him at all you'll put his mind at rest. Do you hear me?' he hissed through gritted teeth.

She stared at him, throat tight with emotion. 'Despite what you think, I love my father very much!' she exclaimed, cut to the quick that he could think her so selfish.

Yet, even as she thought it, she knew she *had* been behaving selfishly. Her father was seriously worried, and all she could think about was not wanting to have her life disrupted! She was ashamed of herself.

'Then do the right thing for once in your life,' he growled in a powerful undertone.

Shelby quivered with emotion, eyes flashing stormily. Oh, how she hated that it was Gray who made her see sense. 'I hate you!'

He smiled mockingly. 'I know. Hell, isn't it? Hating me and yet wanting me?'

Her stomach lurched at the arrogance in his tone. 'I don't want you,' she denied through gritted teeth, but he merely laughed softly.

'I could prove otherwise, but at the moment we have more pressing things to sort out. So, what's it to be?'

As if there was a choice. Shelby loved her father, and would never do anything to hurt him. OK, she didn't take the threat seriously, but all she really needed to know was that he did. That was what she had to think about. 'All right, I'll agree to the bodyguard. Now let me go!'

Having secured her agreement, he released her hand, trailing his fingers over her palm as he did so. The small action made her catch her breath and he smiled knowingly as he straightened up. 'Wise choice. Like it or not, you're stuck with me now,' he added and, much to her chagrin, laughed softly. 'So, tell me, what have you been doing with yourself lately? Still running amok through the local male population?'

Before she could come back with a pithy retort, her father returned with their drinks. 'Here you are, Gray.' He handed over a glass of golden liquid, which the younger man took but didn't immediately touch. 'What are you two talking about? Old times?'

Blue eyes glinted roguishly. 'Actually, I was just asking

Shelby about her love life,' Gray remarked goadingly, and Shelby's heart sank. Her father strongly disapproved of her dating habits.

Oscar Greer snorted. 'Love life? I wouldn't call it that! She's like a butterfly, flitting from man to man, never stopping long enough to find out if there could be a relationship. Whatever she's looking for, she'll never find it going on the way she does.'

'Dad!' Shelby exclaimed in protest, although there was far too much truth in what her father had said. Of course she didn't linger, but there was a reason for that. She wouldn't give false hope to any man. She had already found what she was looking for, and it was a closed door. So she wasn't so much searching as marking time. Catching Gray's mocking glance, she rushed to change the subject. 'Gray doesn't want to hear about my love life.'

Gray quirked an eyebrow at her. 'If you want to keep secrets, try being more circumspect. I learn all I need to from the gossip columns.'

Colour stormed into her cheeks, for those columns were a constant source of misery for her. Unfortunately it was the price of fame. 'You shouldn't believe all you read.' They made her out to be some sort of maneater, which she most certainly wasn't. Far from it, in fact.

'You're just as bad, Gray. You have no staying power either,' Oscar told his right-hand man, and Shelby laughed.

'You tell him, Dad. It's shocking the way he goes on,' she sniped whilst blue eyes threatened retribution.

Her father tsked, though there was a reluctant gleam of humour in the twitch of his lips. 'Sometimes I want to knock both your heads together. When are you going to settle down? The way you're going on, you're both going to end up with nobody.'

Her throat closed over at her father's obvious concern. 'I'll settle down one day, Dad. When I find the right man.'

'He could be under your nose and you wouldn't see him!'

Shelby bit her lip at the unwitting accuracy of his words. Except she had seen him. How could she tell her father the man she wanted hadn't wanted her? 'I'll have my eyes tested, I promise,' she said, attempting to tease him out of his mood. She succeeded, for Oscar Greer patted her hand and smiled at her.

'I'm nagging, I know, but it's a father's prerogative to worry about his daughter.'

'Speaking of which,' Gray inserted swiftly, 'Shelby has something she wants to tell you,' he declared, shooting her a pointed look.

Having been put on the spot, Shelby cleared her throat and looked at her father. 'I've, er, been talking to Gray, and we…that is, *I* realise I've been behaving stupidly. So…' She took a deep breath and dived in. 'I'll agree to the bodyguard,' she ended on a rush. Glancing at Gray, she set her jaw. 'Happy now?'

Fortunately her father chose not to question the how of it, but sent her a broad smile of relief. 'Thank you, darling. That's a weight off my mind. I didn't know how I was going to get through this if you kept on refusing to see sense.'

Which made her feel even more guilty than she had been. 'Yes, well, Gray made me see things more clearly,' she enlarged uncomfortably, and Oscar looked past her to the younger man.

'Thank you, Gray.'

'My pleasure.'

'We should sit down and talk about tactics,' her father said, urging them towards the comfortable chairs and couches ranged around the fireplace. Shelby took a seat at the other end of the couch from Gray and waited to hear her fate.

'It goes without saying that we put ourselves entirely in your hands,' Oscar told the younger man the moment they were all seated.

Shelby immediately saw a flaw. 'Hang on a second. I know I've agreed in principle, but I'd like to know what qualifies Gray for the job before I hand myself over to him on a plate.'

One eyebrow quirked lazily. 'Don't you trust me, Red? I'm hurt. I thought you knew better.'

She knew what he was referring to, and it was just like him to throw that in her face. Of course, he had no idea of the real blow he had dealt her, for she had licked her wounds in private, and still did. Her palm itched to slap him, but all she did was send him a narrow look. 'I was wondering what qualifications you could possibly have for this job,' she shot back. It was, after all, a reasonable question.

'I wear many hats, Red. Amongst other things, I am a security expert. If you want my credentials, all I can tell you is that I learnt my trade in the forces.'

'You were in the army?' That came as a total surprise. She immediately had visions of him doing the daring sort of things she had seen done in numerous Hollywood movies.

He shrugged lightly. 'You know how it is with boys; we never get over playing with our toy soldiers.'

'I never saw you playing with soldiers,' Shelby pointed out. 'And what you're talking about is hi-tech stuff. That's not just ordinary soldiering. It sounds more…covert.' The notion intrigued her. 'What sort of things did you do?'

Gray suddenly looked amused. 'As they say in all the best movies, I could tell you but then I'd have to kill you,' he said with a wry grin.

Her father laughed. 'Suffice it to say he is eminently qualified for the job, Shelby.'

In her heart of hearts she knew it. Gray had always been the kind of man who did well at whatever he chose to take on. It was time to give in as gracefully as possible. 'OK, OK, point taken. So what happens next?'

All laughter vanished as Gray's expression grew serious. 'We become joined at the hip, for however long it takes.'

That sounded awfully intimate—something that didn't sit well with her at all. She frowned at him. 'I understood you would be watching me from a distance.'

To her dismay he shook his head. 'Then you understood wrongly. If I'm to be of any use, then I have to be on hand twenty-four-seven.'

Shelby had a sinking feeling in the pit of her stomach. 'By 'on hand' you mean…?'

Gray's smile reappeared, laden with mockery. 'Just what you think I mean, Red. I'll be moving into your spare room for the duration.'

At that point Shelby closed her eyes. It was her worst nightmare. She could handle her feelings for Gray at a distance, but having him in her own home would mean that after this was all over he would be imprinted in her rooms. She would be able to imagine him there, and her sanctuary would no longer exist. Yet what could she do? Creating a scene was out of the question now that she had agreed to have the bodyguard. She was doomed.

Or was she? There was, of course, one other possibility. Perhaps she was just dreaming all this, and when she woke it would all fade away. When she really opened her eyes, Gray would be gone and her life would be back to normal again.

Her despairing thoughts were interrupted by the ringing of the telephone and she opened her eyes to see her father crossing the room to answer it. Gray, meanwhile, sat watching her from the opposite end of the couch. It wasn't a dream. It was for real.

'Sorry to disappoint you, but I'm still here,' he told her, clearly knowing exactly what she had been thinking.

Deeply rattled, Shelby crossed one silk-clad leg over the other and crossed her arms to match. 'You're enjoying this, aren't you?' she challenged with a basilisk glare.

Gray didn't laugh. 'I see nothing amusing in protecting you from being seriously hurt...or worse.'

Shelby tapped out a tattoo on her arm with her fingers. 'You can't possibly take it all seriously.'

That, if anything, made him look grimmer. 'Better that than to do nothing and live with the consequences. I've been down that road, and I'll tell you this for nothing—it isn't going to happen again!'

Shelby's lips parted on a tiny gasp of surprise. This was an unexpected revelation. 'What do you mean? What happened?'

Now his mouth twisted into a bitter smile as he shook his head. 'You don't want to know. The important thing is that I'm going to be doing everything in my power to prevent anything like it happening to you!'

She pressed a hand to a suddenly queasy stomach. His message got through loud and clear. 'Why? I mean, what do you care what happens to me?'

'I care because your father is a good man.'

'It's...all for him, then?' For a fleeting moment she had harboured the idea that he might just care about her a little. Her heart suffered another bruise as she realised she ought to have known better.

Gray's eyes looked piercingly into hers for an instant. 'Did you think it would be for you?'

Shelby swallowed her hurt and shrugged. 'Of course not. I know better than that.'

'I'm glad to hear it. After all, why should I care anything for a woman who has done all the things you have?' Gray observed sardonically.

Which, as it happened, was very much what she thought too. She had done nothing to endear herself to him. Why would he fall in love with her, or care anything about her? She had no answer, only wished that, despite everything, he could somehow do both. Flying pigs, though, were in short supply these days. So she rallied her spirit and responded swiftly.

'Leave my past out of this, Gray!' she commanded sharply, making him shake his head again.

'I can see why you would want to. It's not very flattering.'

No, it wasn't, but she had worked hard to live it down. A fact he chose to overlook. 'I'm trying to put all that behind me,' she insisted, and he gave her a measuring look.

'Well, now. Let's hope you live long enough to do it. Which brings us back to why I'm here.'

Before Shelby could say anything more, her father rejoined them.

'Sorry about that. Now, where were we?' he asked as he made himself comfortable in his chair once more.

'I'd just told Shelby that I would be moving into her spare room.'

Oscar shot her a quick glance. 'How did she take it?'

Gray's lips twitched. 'About as well as we expected.'

Shelby rolled her eyes. 'Will you please stop talking about me as if I'm not here?' she commanded in exasperation. 'I have the right to make the important decisions about my life.'

'That's good, because you've already made the most important one. You agreed with your father's decision to ask for my help,' Gray put in swiftly. 'And, as I told you, I'm not going to let anything happen to you, Red,' he added in the quietly confident way of his that had the uncanny knack of calming the nerves in her stomach immediately.

She stared at him hard, trying to penetrate those devilish blue eyes. 'That's a promise, is it?'

'Cross my heart,' he retorted, making the gesture to confirm it.

However much she trusted him when it came to his work, Shelby wasn't going to appear to be won over too quickly. 'Do you really have to move in to do it? Couldn't you... oh, I don't know...surveille—is that a word?—the house from a plain vehicle or something?' she suggested rather wildly in a last-ditch attempt to retrieve her privacy.

Not surprisingly, Gray's brows had risen as she meandered on and by the end he was frowning. 'You've been watching far too many movies. Trust me, I know what's needed.'

'And you need to be in my home.' It was a flat statement rather than a question. Gray answered it anyway.

'Following your every step like Peter Pan's shadow.'

That was hardly designed to improve her mood, and she knew it was a deliberate goad. She was going to have to resign herself to his being there for some time, and the worst of it was that she was still convinced the whole thing was a waste of time. However, her father feared the worst, and she wasn't about to add to his worries. She could do this for him.

'How long will it take you to get your things together?' Shelby enquired with a heavy heart.

'I have everything I need in the boot of my car, so I'll be ready to leave whenever you are,' he informed her, and her hope that he would delay his arrival until the next day was dashed.

Her father was all smiles. 'You'll be staying to dinner, I hope, now that everything's decided?'

Gray looked to Shelby, one eyebrow raised questioningly. 'Unless Shelby wants to go home now?'

Had she been going alone she would have decided to

leave, but as that was impossible she decided to drag out the moment as long as she could.

'Oh, I'll be having dinner here,' she responded, making a show of settling herself comfortably for a long stay. 'I never miss the chance of eating one of Mrs Grundy's meals.'

Oscar Greer rubbed his hands together. 'You're in for a treat, my boy,' he declared as he stood up yet again. 'I'll just go and tell Mrs G to set another place. I won't be long.'

Silence fell as he left the room, and, as if to balance that out Shelby became intensely aware of Gray's physical presence. From the corner of her eye she could see his hand resting on his knee, and her heart twisted. It recalled the precise moment when she had fallen in love with him. He had offered her a hand to help her out of a taxi, and the touch had been like magic. Exactly as they said it felt in the movies, only for real. She had known then that Gray was special. What the movies hadn't said was that it didn't have to be mutual. From his behaviour, Gray had clearly felt nothing, whilst she had suffered an emotional sea change. She had been eighteen then and, ten years later, her feelings hadn't changed one iota. He was still that special someone and she was still lonely.

'So,' Gray said conversationally, drawing her out of her reverie and making her glance his way. 'Here we are. Together again.'

Shelby laughed harshly and looked at him askance. 'I'd hardly call us together. We just happen to be in the same room.'

A reply that had his blue eyes gleaming with devilment. 'I recall a time when a situation like this was just what you wanted,' he went on, spreading his hands to take in the fact that there were just the two of them.

As was his wont, he was deliberately trying to embarrass her, but she didn't embarrass so easily. 'Well, you were dating every woman within a ten-mile radius. Good Lord, they were falling over themselves to be next in line, so I thought I might as well see what all the fuss was about. I got over it.'

He acknowledged that with a tip of his head, and added, 'Cold shower helped, did it? I told you it would.'

Shelby ground her teeth together irritably. 'I just knew you wouldn't be able to resist saying I told you so.'

Her response drew a laugh. 'I would have hated to disappoint you. At least now you know I'm every bit as bad as all the nasty things you called me.'

Shelby started to open her mouth to deny doing any such thing, but he gave her such a look that she thought better of it. 'I hope your ears burned,' she said instead, and his smile reappeared.

'Stung for days afterwards.'

'Good. I'm delighted to hear it. Of course, it was less than you deserved,' she told him haughtily and he pulled a pained face.

'Hmm, I wince at the idea of what you would consider just payment,' Gray declared with a sharp intake of breath, and Shelby laughed this time.

'You're right to be afraid. As far as I'm concerned, there is no statute of limitations on your particular crime,' she informed him with a challenging look.

Gray eyed her thoughtfully, and there was no way she could read what was going on in his fertile mind. 'Looks like I'm in for an interesting assignment, doesn't it?' he said at last, and there was something in the way he said it that sent alarm signals through her system. She couldn't say why, but all of a sudden there was something... dangerous in the air.

Shelby's eyes narrowed suspiciously. 'What are you planning?'

His smile was as innocent as the day was long. 'Why,

just to keep you out of harm's way. What did you think I would do?'

She didn't trust him, especially when he looked so innocent. 'Just remember you're here on sufferance. If it was left up to me, we wouldn't be going through this.'

'Don't worry, I understand perfectly. You're putting your father's mind at rest, and you're accepting my presence under duress,' he summarised for her. 'Correct?'

'Why is it that the instant you start being reasonable, I start to get nervous?'

He grinned broadly. 'Maybe it's something to do with not wanting to be beholden to me for anything. Rest easy, this is for your Dad, not you.'

'Fine. That's fine,' she muttered, silently praying that the whole ridiculous situation would be over soon.

At that fortuitous moment Oscar Greer returned to the room, looking much more cheerful than he had for days. She knew it was Gray's presence which had brought that about, and it confirmed to her that she was doing the right thing. If it would put her father's mind at rest, she would bite the bullet. After all, it wouldn't be for long. She was utterly sure of that.

Why, she was willing to bet that by this time next week Gray Compton would have packed his bags and disappeared from whence he came. Then her life would get back to normal. By that she meant—*Gray Free*. Which wasn't the way she wanted it, but it was how it was doomed to be.

CHAPTER TWO

SHELBY drew her car to a halt at yet another red light, and her eyes automatically trained in on the pair of headlights she could see in the rear view mirror. Gray was following her home, matching every turn she made. It had been tempting to draw out the journey by going out of her way, but it also occurred to her that Gray was just the sort of person who would have checked out her route home beforehand. Any deviation she made would be cause for comment, and therefore making her seem childish in the extreme. So she had taken her usual route, constantly aware of those never wavering headlights.

Sitting there in the dark, fingers tapping out a nervy tattoo on the steering-wheel, she imagined she could feel Gray's eyes boring into the back of her head. Not for the first time, she wondered what he was thinking. Did he, for instance, ever think back to the events of that long ago evening, when all her hopes and dreams had come crashing down around her ears?

Of course, it would never have happened if she hadn't been feeling sorry for herself. She had been acting as hostess for one of her father's dinner parties, and had been let down by the man who she was then dating. By coincidence, Gray had turned up without a partner too, which had somehow made her feel that this was her chance. She had been eating her heart out over him for two years, and had still had hopes that a miracle would happen. Sometimes, though, miracles needed a helping hand, and she had decided to make a bold venture. Late on in the evening, when the party had split into groups, she had seen Gray wander out on to the patio. When a quick glance told her that everyone else was accounted for, she had followed him…

A sharp blast from a car horn made Shelby jump violently, pulling her out of her daydream, and she realised she had been sitting there whilst the lights had changed to green. She ground the gears getting the car into first and grimaced at the thought of the smile Gray would be wearing when he heard it. Something similar to the one he had worn when he had held her away from him after she had attempted to kiss him that night. But she was getting ahead of herself.

When she had joined him in the relative privacy of the patio, he had turned to face her, resting one hip against the low wall of the parapet.

'Lost your way, Red?' he asked her lightly and she shrugged, though she was feeling far from relaxed. 'You don't usually seek me out these days.'

She shook her head as she slowly walked towards him, trembling hands linked loosely behind her back. 'Things change.'

His lips twitched and one eyebrow quirked rakishly. 'In what way?'

'As we're the only ones without partners, I thought we could be company for each other,' she told him, reaching out to brush off a non-existent piece of debris from the front of his dinner jacket.

'Did you now?' he responded suavely and, gathering her resolve, Shelby took a small step towards him, closing the gap, placed both hands on his chest and looked up at him seductively.

'Um-hm. It's too good an opportunity to miss. Here we are, just you, me and the night. It's perfect for getting to know one another better,' she insisted in a sultry voice that carried a tremor of anticipation. She tried to caress his cheek, but he foiled her plan, holding her wrist in a light yet unremitting grip.

'How much have you had to drink, Shelby?'

She sighed, smiling. 'Just enough to blunt the edges. Come on, Gray, relax, let yourself go a little,' she urged him, her eyes locked on the lips she longed to kiss.

She didn't see his eyes narrow. 'And do what...seduce you?'

'Sounds like a plan,' she agreed, and would have put her arm around his neck only he abruptly pushed her away.

'What the hell do you think you're doing, little girl?' he demanded mockingly, finally bursting the delicious bubble she had been floating in.

'Little girl?' she gasped, cut to the quick. 'I'm twenty years old. That makes me a woman, not a girl!'

'You're playing out of your league, Red. Just because your boyfriend stood you up doesn't mean you can practice your seduction skills on me.'

That got through like nothing else, and her hopes and dreams dissolved around her. Yet, smarting though she was, she realised he had at least left her the means to save face. Swallowing hard, she covered her retreat with style. 'I should have known you wouldn't want me, but you can't blame a girl for trying!' she retorted ruefully, stepping away from him.

He shook his head. 'You're going to give your father grey hairs before his time. A fact you might want to re-member. Seducing the boss's daughter is a non-starter.'

The remark rubbed salt into the wound, but she battled on bravely. 'Is that all that stopped you? Listen, we wouldn't have to tell him.'

'Sorry, Red, but I'd know. Besides, you're too young for me. If I was looking to be seduced tonight, it would be by a woman who knows what she's doing,' he added for good measure, making her feel worse.

At the same time she was relieved that he was falling for her ploy. He would never know how deep the wounds went, or how much blood he had drawn. 'For a man who's known for his charm, that wasn't very subtle, Gray. But there's no harm done. I won't bother you again.' So saying, she returned to the house.

Rejoining the other guests, she stayed there, not looking up when Gray came back in, although she was aware of him with every nerve in her body. She held it all together until everyone had gone. Then she retreated to her room and sobbed into her pillow.

Only when the tears of despair and mortification had dried up had she been grateful that her feelings for him had remained secret. She had pulled off a feat of acting that was worthy of an award. Amazingly, her love for him hadn't withered under the blow. It had been too strong for that.

It still was, Shelby conceded as she stopped briefly at a junction, then turned right. The headlights followed her. She hadn't seen Gray for a while after that. She had braced herself for days for that inevitable first meeting, only to be told by her father that he had gone abroad again. When he had returned, she had had her protective armour in place. She had battled with him just as she always had, and that one small incident had faded into history.

In fact, it was only at moments such as these that she thought of it at all, she mused as she drove through a one-way system. Of course, there had been that second, more devastating meeting between them later, but she tried not to think of that. Bad enough to go through it once, why choose to relive it in glorious Technicolor? Better to concentrate on her driving.

A short while later she turned down the ramp of the underground car park belonging to the modern block of apartments in which she lived. Using her remote control, she opened the security gates and drove through. Parking in her reserved spot, she climbed out and indicated that Gray should park beside her. The spot belonged to a neighbour who was working abroad for the next few months. Shelby collected her bag and set the car alarm.

Gray, meanwhile, had alighted from his four-by-four and was rummaging around in the back. Having retrieved what he wanted, he walked round to join her. 'Tell me, do you always take the same route home?'

'From Dad's? Yes, of course. I've found it's the quickest,' Shelby confirmed, then frowned when he looked concerned.

'Forget the quickest. From tomorrow you start varying your routes. Especially places you go to frequently. Nothing will help this creep more than your own habits,' he informed her bluntly, then looked around him. 'How do we get in?'

'The lifts are over here.' She pointed off to her right and was surprised when Gray slipped a hand under her elbow and urged her along. 'Hey…'

'This isn't personal. I'm not holding you because I want to.'

'I know that,' she shot back scornfully. 'You're under orders again.'

He shot her a narrow look. 'We'll never get beyond that, will we?'

'Not in this life or the next,' she confirmed scathingly and he made a grunting sound in his throat.

'Let's hope the next life doesn't come along sooner than you expect!' Gray returned dryly.

Shelby looked at him in shock. 'Surely this nut case wouldn't try to kill me?' she asked in some alarm.

To her dismay he didn't play that down with a laugh. 'Don't worry. I'm here to make sure he never gets the chance.'

She frowned as her confidence took a knock. 'But this is just a scam!'

Gray's smile was tight. 'Let's hope you're right, but in the meantime I'm taking no chances. I never like to see mistakes repeated.'

'Mistakes?' She knew instantly he was referring to that security situation which had gone wrong. 'What happened?'

'Let's just say someone died, and it wasn't pretty. Now, I've imagined seeing you in all sorts of situations, but never lifeless at my feet. I'd prefer to keep it that way,' Gray returned dryly, not about to be drawn.

Shelby found the remark at once surprising and intriguing. It was rather comforting to know he didn't want to see her harmed, but what were these other ways he had pictured her? Her mind reeled but could find no answer. By which time they had reached the lift.

'OK, if you have gates on the garage, can I assume there's a doorman inside the lobby?' Gray wanted to know as he jabbed the call button.

She was glad she could confirm that much at least. 'Twenty-four hour cover, taken in shifts. It was one of the reasons I took this apartment,' she added pointedly. He might think she wasn't security conscious, but in this day and age it was silly not to be.

He looked at her, one eyebrow raised quizzically. 'Glad to hear you've got some sense then, Red. I was beginning to wonder.'

Shelby shot him a sideways glare. 'Did you have to work hard at getting so rude, or did it come naturally?' she gibed, but could have saved herself the effort for it was like water off a duck's back.

'Naturally, of course,' he confirmed mockingly. The lift arrived and they stepped inside. 'Which floor?'

'The top.' As she had known she wouldn't have a garden, she had settled for a view.

The doors closed and they began the nearly silent ascent.

Gray's lips twitched. 'How do you resist calling it the penthouse? I would have thought it would add to your mystique.'

She rolled her eyes heavenwards. 'I'm sure it hasn't escaped your notice that there are only six floors, Gray. To call the top the penthouse would make me look ridiculous.'

He didn't allow her to get away with that. 'So, what do you call it?'

Shelby frowned and shifted from foot to foot uncomfortably. She didn't want to tell him, for she knew in her bones he would laugh and call it pretentious. 'Who says I call it anything?'

'Because I know the way you think. To your father it's the top right apartment, but to the clients you want to impress you'd call it something much more upmarket,' Gray eyed her consideringly. 'It would have to be something arty. Something like...*pied-à-terre*.'

Her eyes narrowed suspiciously as he hit the nail squarely on the head. 'You knew. Dad told you!' she exclaimed, unwilling to believe he would think of it himself.

As ever, he found her vastly entertaining, and laughed. 'Not a bit of it. I had a lucky guess. But you've disappointed me, Red. I didn't imagine you would be so predictable.'

For an instant Shelby would dearly have loved to give him a predictable thump on his big head! Fortunately for him, she wasn't given to physical violence. 'My clients like it. That's all that counts.'

'Aren't you afraid for your immortal soul?' he asked dryly and, goaded, Shelby snapped.

'I'll hit you in a minute!'

Gray laughed even more heartily. 'Now that sounds more

like the Shelby I know. You never used to go in for all this pretentious nonsense.'

'True, but then I wasn't trying to earn a living,' she told him caustically, wondering how she was ever going to get through the next few days with her sanity intact.

The lift arrived at the top and deposited them on to the landing. There were three doors leading off the small area. Two were clearly to apartments, the other was the fire escape. Gray examined it carefully, then nodded, satisfied.

'Who lives opposite and below you?' he wanted to know next, and Shelby quickly got herself together.

'Opposite are a married couple in their thirties. They both have high-powered jobs. I don't see much of them. Tim lives below me, but he's abroad for the next few months. You're parking in his space. Why?'

Gray didn't look too happy with what she told him. 'That leaves you pretty much isolated up here. Let's go inside so I can have a quick look around.'

Shelby reached into her bag for her keys, feeling ever so slightly on edge. She had felt perfectly safe up until he started shaking his head at what he saw. OK, she still didn't believe anything was going to happen, but he was certainly putting the wind up her. Opening the door to apartment 6A, she would have walked in, except that Gray quickly caught her arm and held her back.

'I'll go first, to be on the safe side.'

Jittery or not, so far as Shelby was concerned that was going too far. 'Oh, come on. There's nobody in there,' she protested, and drew a cool look from her companion.

'You'd better start thinking defensively, or you're asking for trouble,' Gray advised sternly and walked past her, dropping his bag just inside the hallway before switching on the light.

No doubt to have both hands free to deal with whatever came his way. Shelby thought irritably. Trust him to talk about her being pretentious, when he was acting like some comic book hero.

She stepped inside, closing the door behind her, and when she turned round again all thought of intruders—real or imagined—vanished. Shelby found she had an unobstructed view of Gray striding away from her and, quick as a flash, her mouth went dry as a wave of heat swept over her. The cause of this rush of longing was totally unaware that, with his leather bomber jacket resting on his hips, she had the perfect view of his long legs and extremely sexy physique. His walk had an animal quality about it, and it made her decidedly weak at the knees.

Oh, boy, she thought as he disappeared into her lounge, and groaned helplessly. She couldn't recall ever being turned on so quickly, and he hadn't even touched her. Yet she had known for years that Gray had that certain something which no other man had. Just being near him was enough to set her pulse racing. Out of necessity she had become adept at hiding her reaction, but the situation she found herself in was far beyond the norm. She was going to have to be on her guard not to let anything slip.

Shelby was bracing herself to walk forward when Gray reappeared in the hallway as if he had been magicked there. Whereupon Shelby was struck by another pulse of awareness. She hadn't felt it so keenly at her father's house, but now they were alone in her apartment it was another matter. The instinctual female side of her was vitally aware of the pure maleness of him. He exuded a particularly potent brand of sexuality that struck a chord, and her whole body thrummed in reply. She pulled a face as she acknowledged that functioning naturally might be a problem.

Gray's expression, however, was stony. 'I told you to stay outside.'

Shelby tensed immediately, not caring for his tone. 'I

heard you, but this is my home and you can't order me around in it.'

Unimpressed, he took a step closer. 'I give the orders here, and you will do what I say when I say. Is that clear?'

Anger surged inside her, and Shelby instinctively took a step back. 'You can't browbeat me. I'm not scared of you, Gray Compton!' she raged, and his lip curled.

'Trust you to get things backwards. It's the man out there you should be afraid of and, until you get that through your thick head, I'm going to be doing my best to keep you safe in spite of yourself!' he growled back and stooped to pick up his bag.

When he straightened up they were virtually nose to nose. Quick as a flash, Shelby found her heart was suddenly going at a gallop, and almost groaned. Get a grip, you idiot, she thought, taking herself firmly to task. You don't want him to see how strongly you're still attracted to him.

Meeting his gaze, she noted there was a glint in his eye which she didn't like the look of. 'By the way, if you're still hungry, try looking in the kitchen. I'm not on the menu tonight,' he drawled mockingly, and her heart lurched as she realised she hadn't acted swiftly enough. He had seen far too much.

'I wouldn't want you even if you were,' she denied at once, only to find herself being observed in sardonic amusement.

'That's not the message your eyes were sending out a minute ago. You still want me.'

The very fact that she knew it was true meant she had no option but to fight a rearguard action. 'Why would I do anything so puerile?'

He shrugged. 'Probably because I'm the one who got away. That's not supposed to happen. You have to put the record straight.'

Appalled that he could think she would have to have him

solely to salve her pride, Shelby hastened to deny it.
'You're out of your mind!'

His lips twitched, revealing his hidden amusement.
'Shame. I was toying with the idea of maybe letting you
catch me this time,' he said as he turned away. 'Do you
have a security system?'

Stunned into silence by his offhand remark, Shelby followed him as he retraced his steps, switching on more lights
as he went. 'What do you mean, you might let me catch
you?' she charged, finding her voice at last.

'It was just a thought. I'd have to decide whether the
joys of sharing a bed with you would be worth all the
aggravation of dealing with you out of it before I made up
my mind,' he enlarged mockingly.

That was a red rag of the largest kind. Of all the…! She
was beside herself. How dared he assume she'd simply fall
into his arms. 'Oh, you would, would you? Well, let me
tell you something, Gray. It isn't up to you. If I caught you
I'd throw you right back! Do you know why?'

He tipped his head as he looked at her. 'I'm sure you're
about to tell me.'

'Because, after what you did, I could never trust you
again. You lied to me, and you used me,' she declared
fervently, feeling the pain of betrayal even as she spoke,
and he smiled grimly.

'I regretted having to do it, but it was necessary,' he
countered tersely and she laughed harshly.

'Is that an apology?'

Blue eyes searched hers. 'Would it make a difference if
it was?' he asked and her chin went up.

'No,' she said with cutting finality, and saw a muscle
tense in his jaw for a moment before he sighed heavily.

'You speak with absolute certainty, yet it doesn't appear
to have stopped you wanting me,' he reminded her, bringing a faint wash of colour to her cheeks.

As he knew already, there was no point in denying it. 'Obviously not, but I'm not about to give in to temptation. However attractively packaged.'

That had him shaking his head. 'So it's a case of looking but not touching, is it?' he asked mockingly. 'Think you can keep to the rules?'

A cruel smile curved her lips. 'Oh, yes. All I have to do is think back to that night, and there's no problem. So dream on. I'm not for sale at any price!'

Gray smiled back. 'Everyone has their price, Red. I'll just have to find yours. If I decide I want to take the matter further, that is. For the moment just try and keep your mind on the matter at hand. You can dream about me later. Now, let's get back to the security system. Do you have one?'

It irked her no end that he had to have the last word. But there was no real harm done. So what if he knew she was still physically attracted to him despite everything that had happened? It wasn't the end of the world. He didn't know she loved him, and that was how it had to stay. Taking a steadying breath, she concentrated her mind on what he had asked her.

'Security system? Yes, there is one, but I never use it. The man on the desk is supposed to stop unwanted guests,' she told him, and Gray stared at her incredulously.

'Mercy, but you're not safe to be let out without a keeper! Do you have any sense of self-preservation? Uninvited guests don't arrive by the front door. From to-morrow you start using it,' he decided for her.

She didn't see the point, but no doubt he'd be reporting to her father and he'd blow his top, which wasn't what she wanted, so Shelby took a deep breath and nodded. 'All right, but I wish to goodness you'd stop barking orders at me. Don't you know you catch more flies with honey?'

'Your point being?'

'You could try asking me instead of telling me. After

all, I'm only doing this for Dad, not because I take it seriously.'

Gray folded his arms and observed her thoughtfully. 'I can't make up my mind if you're being wilfully stupid or you really are that naive. What will make you take it seriously?'

'Nothing you could possibly say. The value of your word has been seriously devalued by your actions,' she told him with a belligerent lift of her chin.

Anger and something else she couldn't name flashed in his eyes and he gritted his teeth. 'OK, Red, I've said it before and this is the last time I'll repeat it. After that, all bets are off. This is what we do. We compromise. Until this proves to be the damp squib you insist it is, we play the game my way. Agreed?'

'And if I don't?'

His smile was grim. 'You won't be leaving this apartment any time soon. It's up to you.'

Knowing he would do it too, Shelby eyed him scathingly. 'So, you'd add kidnapping to the list of your crimes, would you? It doesn't surprise me. I know the lengths you'll go to for Dad.'

Blue eyes flashed dangerously. 'You know nothing, Red. Maybe I have a vested interest in keeping you alive.'

She shrugged indifferently. 'Course you do. You want to keep your job!'

Gray muttered something dire under his breath. 'If you want to find out how far you can push me, sweetheart, keep this up,' he threatened darkly and, having got the result she wanted, Shelby subsided.

'I had no idea you were so touchy,' she murmured, dropping down on to the nearest couch. 'Well, this wasn't how I planned to spend the evening.'

'Sorry if I'm cramping your style, but it brings me to my next point,' Gray responded as he walked to the windows and closed the curtains. Turning to face her, he folded his arms across his chest. 'I was going to suggest you tell your current boyfriend not to come calling for the duration. You can do without for a few days, can't you?' he enquired with less than subtle irony, and Shelby tensed instantly.

She couldn't believe what she had just heard. Was he really asking what she thought he was? 'What exactly can I do without?' she demanded to know in a voice icy enough to do serious damage to brass monkeys.

He had the nerve to quirk an eyebrow at her. 'I was referring to male company in general. Look at it this way. A couple of days abstinence could do wonders for your love life.'

Shelby closed her eyes and counted to ten. 'For your information, there's nothing wrong with my love life,' she told him through gritted teeth and he grinned.

'I'm happy for you. Truly,' he returned sardonically, and she very nearly threw something at him. 'So, can you put the boyfriend off?'

She stared him squarely in the eye. 'You know, two can play at this game. How's your love life, Gray? Can *you* do without female company for a few days?'

His response was to wince dramatically. 'Ouch, I think I hit a sore spot. Something tells me you're between men right now.'

She shot to her feet in righteous wrath. 'And you're dicing with death!'

Gray rocked back on his heels, blue eyes gleaming mockingly. 'It never takes long to get that volatile temper of yours to ignite, does it?' he said, and Shelby balled her hands into fists at her sides.

'Not where you're concerned, no,' she agreed snappily. 'I think you delight in doing it.'

'You've discovered my secret,' he confirmed lazily. 'It

always fascinated me to see what happened when I lit the blue touch-paper.'

This time she raised an eyebrow at him. 'Maybe you should remember the warning advises you to retire immediately.'

'Oh, I've fantasised about that many a night,' he revealed huskily, holding her gaze, and a wave of heat surged through her. Suddenly the air between them was charged with electricity and her wayward senses couldn't help responding. This was how it had been that other time, when she had fallen for his charming brand of lies. He had made her believe he was really interested in her and, because she had wanted it to be true, she had plunged headlong. Now, as then, she could no more be indifferent to him than she could stop breathing. Yet she wasn't about to fall under his spell, no matter how much she still wanted him, for she was wise to the games he played. With Gray, nothing was as it seemed.

'I don't wish to know that!' she said with a shudder.

'Have you never fantasised about me?' he went on, amusement dancing in his eyes.

'I might have once, but now it would give me bad dreams!' she declared, and he smiled wryly.

'God forbid that dreams of me should give you nightmares!' Gray exclaimed mockingly, walking over to the sideboard and leaning against it. 'I must be losing my touch.'

'Not really. I know what you're capable of. There's no length you wouldn't go to.'

'To keep you from harm I'd even walk through fire,' he confirmed, and her heart contracted, for she knew it was his loyalty to her father that drove him, not any finer feeling for herself.

'I doubt even Dad would expect that of you,' she retorted scornfully. 'So you're saved.'

'Actually, Red, I expect it of myself,' he countered a tad sharply, then pushed himself to his feet, shoving his hands into the pockets of his trousers. 'Getting back to where we were, I was serious about putting off the boyfriend. Can you do that?' He was all business again, and that tiny moment of exasperation was forgotten.

Shelby wished she didn't have to answer. She could see his point. A boyfriend entering into the equation could make things awkward. It was just that her answer was going to make him even more obnoxious. Not that she had a choice.

Squaring her shoulders, she admitted the truth. 'Actually, I'm not seeing anyone just now.'

Which response brought a flash of amusement. 'That must have been hard to say,' he commiserated. 'That's one problem solved.'

She could have let it go at that but she didn't. 'How about you? Can you forgo a few days of slavish devotion?'

His smile took on a rakish edge. 'Just so happens, sweetheart, that I'm in the same boat you are. Nobody to miss me. Nobody to share those special little moments with.'

Shelby's heart was pleased to hear it, which just proved how besotted she was. Aloud, she made a scoffing noise. 'My heart bleeds for you.'

'Careful, Red. Your claws are showing,' he retorted. 'Well, now we've settled the major issues, perhaps you'll show me to my room? By the way, I like the décor. Did you do it yourself?'

Shelby was torn between wanting to black his eye for him and feeling a sense of pride that he liked her work. She had spent a lot of time on it. The main room had a sitting area and separate dining area. She had decorated each differently, yet so that they complemented each other. 'Every last brushstroke. Are you surprised?'

One eyebrow quirked. 'That you could do something

useful with your life? Not at all. I always knew you had it in you,' he answered dryly and she ground her teeth.

'How come every compliment you utter ends up as an insult?' she asked aggrievedly.

He sent her a lopsided grin. 'Takes practice, Red. Plenty of practice.'

Shelby sniffed. 'Well, you can stop practising. Trust me on this. You're good enough already,' she told him with heavy irony. If he got any better, he'd probably reduce her to tears. Glancing his way, she found him watching her and her brows rose.

'My room?' he prompted, and she berated herself for allowing him to divert her into forgetting what she was doing.

Without a word, she led the way down the short hallway which gave access to the bedrooms and bathroom.

'Bathroom,' she declared as she passed the first door. 'This is the guest bedroom,' she added, opening the next door along and switching on the light. 'You should be comfortable in there.'

'I'm sure I shall,' he agreed, walking past her to drop his bag on the bed and glance around. 'Very restful. Which room is yours?'

'The one across the hall,' she revealed reluctantly. 'The third bedroom is now my office.' She indicated the door at the end with a nod of her head.

'I'll have a better look around in the morning. There is just one other thing, though. Do you possess a dressing gown you can wear?'

Shelby frowned faintly. 'Yes. Why?'

'Good. It will spare my blushes if we should bump into each other on the way to the bathroom,' he retorted with a glint in his eye.

She caught her breath at that. 'I have my own bathroom,' she pointed out quickly, then had a mental vision of bumping into him in the morning whilst they were both in their night-clothes. Assuming he wore pyjamas. Automatically she looked at him doubtfully, whereupon Gray shook his head.

'Not since I was a small boy,' he responded, looking as if he was having trouble holding back a grin.

Her chin dropped. 'But you can't walk about here…' She waved her hands as words failed her.

'Buck naked?' he supplied for her, and the grin began to tweak the corner of his mouth. 'Don't worry. I thought it would be best not to put temptation in your way, so I brought plenty of boxer shorts with me.'

She underwent a moment of relief before the rest of what he had said struck home. Of all the nerve! 'What do you mean, put temptation in my way? There isn't anything the least bit tempting about you!' Which was a lie.

'That's reassuring. I wouldn't want you to take advantage of the situation and pounce on me,' Gray retorted mockingly, and Shelby had never felt more like hitting him.

'I do not pounce on men,' she informed him, stressing each word.

His response to that was to shake his head. 'That's a shame. You might enjoy it!'

He was running rings around her, and Shelby felt like a floundering fish caught on the end of his line. 'So help me, Gray. If you don't shut up, I'll…' Annoyingly, nothing came to mind and she was left staring at him helplessly.

'You'll what? Slap me? Kiss me?' he suggested, and that last had her stomach turning over and her heart doing a diving flip-flop.

'Why would I want to kiss you?' she demanded to know. 'You're not my type!' she added, and both of them knew it was a downright lie. 'Oh, I knew this was a mistake. I should never have agreed to this ridiculous plan.'

Gray shook his head. 'Too late to back out now, Red.

You gave your word and I'm holding you to it. I respect your father too much to leave him in the lurch. He's had to worry too much about you over the years as it is. If I can take some of it off his shoulders now, I will. So get used to the idea. I'm here to stay for the foreseeable future.' With which reminder he closed the bedroom door in her face.

Shelby was left gaping at the wood impotently. She was tempted to hammer on the door and make him explain what he had just said. But, before she could do so, a tweak of conscience stayed her hand. She didn't have to ask him. She knew she was responsible for more than one of her father's grey hairs.

Retreating into her bedroom, she closed the door gently then rested back against it, chewing her lip. It wasn't comfortable remembering the crazy things she had done. Gray's indifference to her had had a backlash. She had needed to prove to herself that she was attractive. So what if he didn't know she was alive, there were plenty more fish in the sea. She had gone out to catch all she could—and had been very successful at it. Of course, she had thrown a lot back. After all, catching them had been the point. Pretty soon she had known that she could have any man she wanted. All she had to do was crook her finger.

Wincing, Shelby straightened up and shook her head in disbelief at her own behaviour. She had gone off the rails with a vengeance. She had wielded her power like a weapon, elated by the notion that she was invincible. The world was her oyster. So she had partied and played for all she was worth, and ignored every sensible word her father had said in his attempts to bring her to her senses. That hadn't happened until Gray had taken a hand.

She hadn't known that was what he was doing. Her father had had to go away to Europe on business for a month, leaving her alone. Gray had taken to calling in to see how she was doing, and had gradually showed her a side of himself that he had previously reserved for the women in his life. Oh, he had been so good at it. His wicked flirting had drawn her like a moth to a flame. He had charmed her with incredible ease, because her heart was aching for him. So when he had eventually invited her to dinner there had been no thought of saying no. It had been perfect, even down to his goodnight kiss.

Soon they had been having lunch together too, as well as dinner every night. She had been in seventh heaven. His kisses had melted her bones, and made her want so much more, but Gray had told her he didn't want to rush things. Of course, by then she had believed that he really cared for her, and it had been like a dream come true. They had been the happiest few weeks of her life. She had had every hope of them leading to something more as time had gone.

Then her father had returned, and the first thing he had wanted to know was if she was still seeing Nick Colby, a young man he had heartily disapproved of. Shelby had actually forgotten all about him. Hadn't seen him at all since Gray had started calling. So, of course she had told her father that she wasn't.

Her father had swept her into a bear hug and smiled down at her. 'That's wonderful, darling. Gray must have said something right,' he remarked and, seeing her confused expression, went on to explain. 'I asked him to have a word with you whilst I was away. He said he would see what he could do. That young man is worth his weight in gold,' he added cheerfully, and went on to talk about other things.

Shelby scarcely heard him. She was dying inside. Whilst her heart cracked wide open, she acknowledged that Gray certainly had done something. He had lied and connived, pretending to feel something for her when he didn't—all so that she would stop seeing the man her father didn't care for! She had never felt so betrayed. The pain was almost unbearable. The only thing which salved her pride was the knowledge that Gray didn't know the full extent of her feelings for him. He knew she wanted him, but that was all.

So when she went in search of him at his office she was able to face him without falling apart. He looked surprised when she walked in, then his smile of welcome faded under the icy glare she sent him.

'What's up?' Gray asked cautiously, and she laughed harshly.

'The game,' she returned smartly. Unable to sit, she paced backwards and forwards in front of the desk. 'Dad's back. He was awfully pleased when he heard I was no longer seeing Nick. Seems to me you're in for a bonus!' she added, rounding on him, so angry she could scream.

Gray's face had frozen into an expressionless mask. 'Take it easy, Shelby. Things aren't quite what they seem,' he started to say, but she jumped on that immediately.

'You mean he didn't ask you to find a way to make me stop seeing Nick?' she demanded, and the question started a muscle flexing in his jaw.

'Yes, he asked me,' Gray confirmed, and the hurt of it reached the very depths of her.

Her green eyes withered him. 'My God, I despise you. I thought you had some integrity, but then you do this. How far would you have gone, Gray? Would you have slept with me, just to make sure?'

Gray came around the desk to her, but when he would have placed his hands on her shoulders she backed away. He drew in a deep breath. 'I can explain, if you'll let me,' he told her, but she had heard enough.

'What can you say that I would believe? It's all lies. Everything you've said and done has been lies. I wouldn't trust you to tell me what time of day it was.'

She had walked out then, before the emotions she was feeling overtook her. The pain had gone deep but she had cried in private, putting on a brave face for the world. She had been such a fool, believing his lies, but it wouldn't happen again. Yet for all she hated him for what he had done, stopping loving him wasn't so easy.

One good thing had come out of it, though. She had made important decisions to change her life. Much to her father's relief, she had stopped partying, finished college and put that part of her life behind her for good.

As for Gray, she could neither forgive nor forget. Nor stop wanting him, if tonight was anything to go by.

Telling herself she was a hopeless case, Shelby sighed and kicked off her shoes. Her shoulders and neck ached with the tension the last few hours had induced, but she had a cure for that. Stripping off her clothes, she padded into the *en suite* bathroom to shower, standing under the warm spray until most of the tightness had gone. Then she dried herself and slipped into a thigh-length strappy silk nightie. About to head to the kitchen for a drink, she remembered just in time that she was not alone, and slipped into the silk robe she kept hanging on the bathroom door.

Locking up as she went, she finally made it to the kitchen and made herself a cup of herb tea. Then she headed back towards her bedroom, coming to an abrupt halt in the middle of the lounge when she saw Gray prowling around. He had stripped off his coat and was wearing a sleeveless black vest that showed off his muscular arms and chest. As she had only ever seen him fully clothed before tonight, Shelby found her eyes riveted to the powerful chest and broad shoulders and her stomach twisted as her senses responded to the sensual male lure.

Gray had stopped also, and now stood with hands braced on his hips as he studied her in his turn. 'Nice robe,' he told her after a second or two. 'Doesn't hide much, but I guess you know that already.'

Actually, Shelby hadn't known anything of the sort and her nerves skittered rather deliciously at his words. However, she did drop a hand to her waist, checking that the belt was still securely tied. Then she stood her ground. No man was going to make her run for cover like a blushing schoolgirl.

'Did you expect me to be wearing one of those neck to toe winceyette ones my granny used to have?'

A wolfish twitch of the lips came and went. 'Not any more,' he declared wickedly. 'This is a much better idea. You always did have a body to die for, Red,' Gray observed reminiscently, and her blood started to pulse thickly through her veins.

She hid her response behind a challengingly raised eyebrow. 'Strange, I don't remember you struggling to keep your hands off it.' Quite the contrary. When he had kissed her, he had been careful not to go too far. At the time, she had been touched by this sign of caring. Later, she had realised it was due to the fact that he didn't really want a physical relationship with her.

Gray shrugged a shoulder. 'The situation was an awkward one for me. It didn't mean I wasn't attracted to you. No red-blooded male could fail to want you, and I'm as red-blooded as the next man. However, I had to be cautious.'

Shelby laughed dryly. 'I know. If you went too far you could have lost your job. That was a narrow line you were treading, trying to keep both of us sweet!' she returned with derision.

This time he smiled wryly. 'You'll never know how many cold showers I had over you.'

She wasn't foolish enough to believe that. 'Sure, and you probably had a lot of sleepless nights, too.'

'More than my fair share, as it happens,' he returned smoothly, but she didn't believe that either.

'You never lost sleep over me, Gray. You didn't care enough about me for that!' It hurt to say it, so she quickly changed the conversation. 'What are you doing out here, anyway?' she asked curiously.

'Same as you, Red. Admiring the view,' he replied mockingly. 'Have you seen enough, or would you like me to take off something else?' he came back wickedly.

Her eyes flashed at him over the top of the mug as she took a sip to moisten a mouth gone suddenly dry. A reckless part of her urged her to call his bluff, but she resisted it. 'I'll pass, if you don't mind. Leave me with my fantasies. Reality turns out to be disappointing.'

'Strange, that wasn't the message I was getting a moment ago,' Gray countered, and she laughed.

'Put it down to a trick of the light. Now, tell me what you were really doing. I thought you were going to bed,' Shelby pointed out.

'Just doing my rounds. Checking the doors and windows are locked for the night.'

'I did that already.'

Gray held up his hands, pacifying her before she took umbrage. 'I'm sure you did, but *I* need to know the apartment is secure.'

She had sense enough to know he was right. She also saw that this was her opportunity to retreat gracefully. 'I'll leave you to it, then. Goodnight.' She crossed the room and thought she had made it safely when his soft words followed her down the hall.

'Sweet dreams,' he said, and Shelby could swear she heard soft laughter follow.

Back in her bedroom, she set the mug of tea down and sank on to the edge of the bed with a groan. Her legs were shaking. This was never going to be an easy situation, but now it was going to be worse. She didn't know what game Gray was playing by telling her he was attracted to her, but she didn't doubt he had a reason. Whatever that reason was, it didn't stop her being drawn to him as strongly as ever.

Going by his past record, she wouldn't put it past him to toy with her precisely because he knew she was still attracted to him. There certainly wasn't anything noble in it. If Gray thought she would fall into his arms like a ripe plum just because he declared an interest, he was mistaken. Not after all he had done.

Unfortunately he could turn up the heat without even trying, because he was so lethally attractive. He didn't even have to touch her to make her want him. All she had to do was close her eyes and she could see him as he was moments ago, standing in her lounge, looking mouth-wateringly good.

Sweet dreams? Oh, no, she wasn't going to have sweet dreams tonight. They were going to be hot and heavy, and very, very sexy!

CHAPTER THREE

ALTHOUGH she hadn't expected to sleep well, Shelby awoke in the morning to realise she must have fallen asleep almost as soon as her head touched the pillow. If she had dreamt of Gray, she didn't remember it. Which was probably just as well.

Feeling remarkably refreshed, she threw back the covers and got up. She had a long day ahead and a meeting with a new client. After that she had to check on an ongoing project. With such a full day in prospect, she knew she would need a good breakfast as she probably wouldn't find time to stop for lunch.

Provided, of course, she was allowed to do so. Gray would be the fly in the ointment.

Cocking her head for sounds of her unwanted guest, she heard nothing and hoped that meant he was still asleep. She knew he intended to dog her footsteps today, but there was no way she could accept that. She'd have to give him the slip. Technically she would be breaking her word, and she experienced a moment's guilt at doing so, but she could see no other way. Her brain started whirring as she stood there, finger tapping her pursed lips. What should she do? In order to outwit him, she would have to move quietly and fast. It was early yet. With any luck she could be out and away before he knew it.

The thought spurred her on to quickly slip into a light-weight silvery-grey trouser suit and a sapphire-blue sleeveless blouse. Combing her hair into a smooth swathe, she applied a light make-up and was ready to go. All she had to do now was find herself something to eat.

Turning the door handle as quietly as possible, Shelby carefully opened the door.

'Going somewhere?' a voice asked mildly and, totally unprepared for it as she was, she let out a shriek loud enough to wake the dead.

Pressing a shaking hand to her chest, where her heart still thundered like a trip-hammer, Shelby positively glowered at Gray, who was leaning nonchalantly against the door post of her spare bedroom. 'You scared the life out of me! What kind of stupid game are you playing?'

'The very question I was just about to ask you,' Gray responded. He was fully dressed in dark trousers and a white T-shirt that clung to his body like a second skin and outlined every toned muscle of his chest and arms. It also showed off his tanned skin perfectly. A fact her senses noted with every sign of pleasure, judging from the way her own skin prickled and the nerves in her stomach tensed. So much so that it was hard to drag her eyes away—again.

She managed it eventually and rushed to her own defence. 'I'm not playing any sort of game,' she denied, a faint wash of guilty colour staining her cheeks. 'You were the one who was lurking!'

Pushing himself upright, Gray folded his arms across his chest, a move that only served to emphasis the leashed power of the man to Shelby. He had the kind of body a woman could fantasise about exploring, she decided appreciatively, and she should know. She had fantasised about him countless times over the years. At which point she caught herself up sharply when she realised where her thoughts were wandering. This was neither the time nor the place.

'You might call it lurking, sweetheart. I prefer to call it waiting.'

Knowing she was in the wrong, her only defence was

attack. 'OK, what were you *waiting* for?' she asked sharply, chin raised at a jaunty angle.

'Knowing you as I do, I was waiting for you to do something just like this. Where do you think you were going, Red?'

She saw no reason to confirm his suspicions that she had been making a bid to escape him. 'If you must know, I was heading for the kitchen to get some breakfast,' she lied, and started to do that very thing.

Stepping forward with the intention of brushing past him, she discovered that Gray had other plans. He refused to budge. Shelby found her eyes were level with the cleft in his chin. Which meant she only had to angle her head slightly to see his mouth, and somehow she couldn't stop herself doing it.

He had a beautiful mouth. Very male, very tantalising. She had yearned to kiss him again for years, and his closeness sent a shiver of anticipation through her. How would his mouth feel now? she wondered. Would he respond if she were to press her lips to his? Not that she was about to put it to the test. Oh, no. She might long to know, but she had more sense than to show it.

'Cut out the games, Red. Where were you going *after* breakfast?' Gray's frosty tone cut through her musings.

Shelby started guiltily and glanced up, licking her lips in a tiny betraying gesture. Shock ran through her when she saw his eyes drop and follow the movement. Captivated, she tried it again, with the same result. She gasped mentally. In her experience, when a man looked that closely at a woman's mouth it meant he was thinking of kissing her. Could Gray really be thinking that?

Of course, she had to meet his eyes to check it out, and found their blue depths regarding her impatiently. 'Don't try to disarm me with your feminine wiles. I want an answer to my question,' he told her in no uncertain terms, emphasising his words so that she jumped.

Her eyes narrowed. 'Why would I use my feminine wiles? They don't work on you, remember?'

Gray laughed sardonically. 'I know full well what your wiles can do, and they work perfectly. Now stop prevaricating and tell me what I want to know!'

It was amazingly hard to think when Gray had just told her that she did have the power to entrance him. It opened up certain unexplored possibilities, but she didn't have time to consider them.

Shelby contrived to shrug casually. 'I was going to work, of course.'

'Not without me, you're not,' he corrected, equally casually, and her eyes narrowed on his as she frowned.

'You can't go with me.' There was no way. Absolutely no way was he going to work with her.

Gray had other ideas. 'You don't have an option. Either I go with you, or you stay here. Your choice,' he declared firmly, eyes daring her to challenge him on this.

'It's out of the question! You must see that,' she said, appealing for his understanding, but he remained unmoved.

'All I see is that your word doesn't mean very much,' he returned sternly, and the accusation stung, for she knew he had a point. However, this was important so she tried another tack.

'Come on, Gray, be reasonable. I've more than met you halfway. I agreed to a bodyguard. I agreed to your staying in my home. But I can't possibly take you with me whilst I visit a new client. How would I explain your presence?' She might have been talking to a block of stone for all the good it did.

'You can make up any sort of story you like for my being there, but I *will* be there,' he said in a tone that brooked no further argument.

Shelby closed her eyes and counted to ten. What on earth was she going to do with him tagging along at her side? How she would have liked to make a dash for the door, but she knew better than to try. Not only would it be undignified, but she had little doubt that he was stronger and faster than she was. He *would* keep her here by force if he had to.

Folding her arms, she stared at him in bitter frustration. 'If this is how you treated your other client that time, I'm not surprised they ended up dead,' she flung at him, and was shocked rather than pleased to see the colour drain from his face as he straightened up, body as tense as a bowstring. With instant compunction she knew she had been unfair, but before she could take it back he spoke.

'The victim wasn't a client but a friend, so I would advise you to be careful what you accuse me of,' he informed her in a tone as hard as granite, and she could tell the subject was still raw.

Biting her lip, she looked at him cautiously. 'I'm sorry. That was out of line.'

'It was,' Gray agreed icily. 'You might not give a damn what happens to you, but I do. I'm prepared to lay down my life to keep you safe. What are you prepared to do?'

Her heart lurched. Would he really do that? she wondered, but one look at his uncompromising expression assured her that he would. It made her feel ashamed. Dear God, she loved him despite everything, and the very last thing she wanted was for him to get seriously hurt. What would she do without him in the world? It didn't bear thinking about, so she did the only sensible thing.

She looked at him steadily. 'If I agree to let you come with me, would you promise to take care of yourself too?' she countered, knowing she absolutely would not be able to live with his death on her conscience.

The tension drained out of him visibly at her question,

and his inclination of the head was every bit as ironic as his next words. 'I have no intention of shuffling off this mortal coil any time soon, so you have a deal,' he confirmed, holding out his hand.

After a moment's hesitation, Shelby took it. The contact was brief, but the tingling heat which travelled up her arm and along her veins remained long after he had released her hand and stepped back.

'So, does this mean you're beginning to take the whole thing seriously?' he wanted to know, and she shook her head.

'Not exactly. I might despise you, but I wouldn't want anything really bad to happen to you,' she conceded with an offhand shrug. Gray laughed softly.

'I'm glad to hear it, if more than a little surprised.'

Shelby refused to bite, for she had just thought of something. 'As you're planning on going everywhere I go, then you should know I've arranged to meet friends at a charity function tonight.' She'd been looking forward to it and had no intention of staying home. 'I hope you've brought a decent suit with you. It's black tie.'

Having got her compliance over work, Gray knew when to back off. 'Don't worry. I won't embarrass you.'

For all that she hated him, the part of her that still loved him would never be ashamed to be seen with him, for he always looked gorgeous in a suit. Not that she would ever say as much. 'Hah! You're a constant embarrassment to me. If you weren't a necessary evil, I wouldn't be seen d...' She broke off, realising what she had been about to say.

Gray merely looked amused. 'The whole reason for my being here is so that nobody has to see you dead. Now, weren't you saying something about breakfast?'

'Er, yes,' She nodded, not feeling quite so hungry now. 'Have you eaten?'

'Are you offering to cook for me, Red?'

'In your dreams!'

He followed her down the hall and into the kitchen, and she was aware of him every inch of the way. 'Actually, I ate an hour ago.' He saw her looking round for signs of the meal and tsked. 'Sorry to disappoint you, but I'm fully house-trained, Red. I clean up after myself.'

'That puts you in a minority of men, I imagine,' she responded dryly. Getting a bowl from the cupboard, she filled it with cereal and sliced bananas and strawberries on the top, then added milk.

Gray hooked out a chair from the table, twisted it around and sat down, resting his arms on the back. 'I can do any household chore, including cleaning the toilet.'

'Quite a catch, then!' Shelby riposted, sitting down opposite him. With the width of the table between them she should have felt more at ease but, no matter how big the proportions of the kitchen were, they shrank now that he was in the room. Her awareness of him was growing exponentially and, just as she had feared, she knew she would never be able to eat in here without picturing him as he looked now. Far too attractive and tempting as sin.

To prove it, one lazy eyebrow quirked her way, giving him that devastating rakish look she liked so much. 'You don't think a woman would want me for my looks?'

Clamping down on her responsive senses, she sent him a mocking smile. 'You know you're drop dead gorgeous, so stop fishing for compliments!'

Gray's blue eyes took on an intriguing gleam. 'Isn't that a strange way to describe a man you hate and despise?'

Shelby managed to look him in the eye and keep her colour under control. 'It doesn't exactly thrill me that I still find you attractive,' she told him honestly. 'You might be good to look at, but women want more than a pretty face.

You flit from woman to woman like a bee. The truth is you've got no staying power, Gray.'

He raised a lazy eyebrow questioningly. 'Is that so? I hate to contradict a lady, but you'd be surprised at my constancy.'

Shelby had good reason to look doubtful. 'You're seriously trying to tell me there's one woman out there who's important to you? I don't believe it!' she scoffed.

He accepted that with a tilt of his head. 'Nevertheless, she exists. I fell in love with her a long time ago,' he confirmed, and in an instant her heart felt as if it had been violently wrenched apart.

It was one thing to know he didn't feel anything for her other than a strong physical attraction, it was quite another to know there was someone he did care for. Jealousy was a bitter taste in her mouth. A small voice wanted to cry out: why couldn't it be me? The truth was, the heart went its own way. Obeyed its own rules. Swallowing her dismay, she looked at him curiously.

'Why haven't you snapped her up?' she asked the obvious question, to which he grimaced.

'Unforeseen circumstances keep getting in the way, and our lives went in different directions,' he revealed matter-of-factly.

Shelby frowned. 'She doesn't know how you feel?'

Gray's shrug was resigned. 'I never had the chance to tell her.'

Shelby stared down at her breakfast, feeling strangely sad. If he was to be believed, he was in the same boat she was, caring for someone who didn't know they existed. Secretly she shared a moment of empathy with him.

'I'm sorry,' she said simply, and drew an ironic smile from him.

'Pity for the enemy, Red? That's unlike you,' he taunted,

and the moment of empathy was lost under a flash of anger at his response.

'You're impossible. She doesn't know how well off she is,' she snapped back. 'Without a doubt you'd find a way to stab her in the back. You're very good at manipulating situations.'

'Put it down to my training,' he advised in amusement.

Shelby concentrated on finishing what was left in her dish before shooting him a haughty look. 'I had no idea they taught you to lie and cheat women in the army. Even now I can't imagine you in uniform. How could you stand to be given orders when you like your own way so much?'

Gray rubbed a thumbnail along the ridge of his nose and gave her a wry look. 'I was an officer. Which meant *I* gave the orders.'

Tipping her head, Shelby studied him. 'I suppose I should have guessed. Now I come to think of it, you did have shorter hair for a time. You wear it longer now.'

There was a roguish gleam in his eye as he watched her watching him. 'I like women to run their fingers through it,' he said just a tad huskily, and it sent a tiny shock wave along her nervous system.

The thought having been planted in her brain, Shelby couldn't help but wonder what it would feel like. Silky and full of life, was her guess. Of course, her fingers started to itch to test it out, which was never going to happen. 'Thanks for the heads up, but why are you bothering to tell me of all people?'

Cerulean eyes held hers. 'Oh, let's just say for future reference,' he told her, and now her nerves did a spectacular somersault.

She arched her brows mockingly. 'What makes you think I would ever want to run my fingers through your hair?'

'You might decide to try a spot of seduction again.'

Her heart skipped a beat, even though she knew he was

just playing games again. 'Do I look that stupid to you? Can you really see that happening with the way I feel about you?'

Gray shrugged his shoulders. 'Why not? For all that you profess to despise me, you want me. You were even thinking about kissing me a few minutes ago.'

Shelby caught back a tiny gasp as her nerves jolted in shock. She hadn't been expecting him to say that. 'Was I indeed?' she challenged, and he smiled mockingly.

'We both know what you were thinking. Why didn't you do it?'

She had no idea what the purpose of this game was, only that she didn't find it amusing. 'Been there. Done that. You pushed me away that time, remember?'

'You were slightly the worse for drink. What else could I do?' Gray answered and, just as easily as that, there was an unexpected nuance in the air.

That came from way out in left field, and Shelby shook her head to clear it. 'Hold on a second. Are you trying to tell me that had I not been the slightest tad tipsy, you would have acted differently that evening?'

Gray merely shrugged again. 'We'll never know, will we? You *were* slightly the worse for wine, and I have rules about such things.'

She stared at him with a sinking feeling. To know that the Dutch courage she had needed had worked against her was a bitter pill to swallow. It made her response all the more waspish. 'Very noble, I'm sure.'

Gray stood up and replaced the chair. 'You'd be surprised how noble I can be.'

Still inwardly smarting from his confession, and the knowledge that she had come that close to realising her dream, Shelby rose too. Not that it changed anything. She would only ever have been a substitute for the real thing. True, she hadn't known that at the time. She had gone on dreaming, and he had gone on to perpetrate the heinous crime for which she had sworn never to forgive him. Now he was playing a new game, seemingly intent on getting her to explore with him the attraction they shared. It was a potentially hurtful one—though he didn't know that. He had no idea how deep her feelings for him went. She wanted to keep it that way. Which meant she must not let him get too close. A relationship of any kind was out of the question.

'Was it the same nobility that stopped you kissing me just now? We both know you were thinking about it,' she said, firing his own words back at him, and he didn't deny wanting to kiss her.

'No,' he answered with a shake of his head. 'The fact is, mixing business with pleasure is dangerous. Right now I should be concentrating on protecting you, nothing more. Allowing myself to be side-tracked could get you harmed.'

Oh, he certainly knew all the right things to say to reel a woman in. She played along, waiting to see where this was going. 'I had no idea I had such an unsettling effect on you.' If asked she wouldn't have doubted for a second that he was strong enough to keep both parts of his life separate. Yet here he was implying otherwise.

Gray shook his head wryly. 'I knew you were going to be trouble when you were in your teens. Even then you had the power to break a man's resolve.'

To Shelby, who remembered everything about that time with crystal clarity, this was a total contradiction. 'I thought I was a child without the allure to attract a man like you?' she reminded him curtly.

'I lied,' he returned simply. 'Like I said, you were slightly over the limit, and I have rules. I needed to put you at arm's length in a hurry, and that was the quickest way.'

Late in the day though it was, those words were a small

sop to her pride. To know that he had been acting chivalrously healed a wound. However, there were bigger ones that those words didn't touch.

'So, it was nobility that stopped you taking me to bed the other time, was it?' she said, challenging his reasoning, wondering what he would choose to say in mitigation.

He went still, eyes locking with hers. 'Why don't you tell me?' he countered softly.

Shelby's lip curled. 'I think Dad's orders specifically stopped you from going too far, and you followed them to the letter, didn't you? It didn't bother you whether you had me or not. It was all a means to an end!'

Something flared in the depths of his eyes. 'Oh, I wanted you, Red, make no mistake about that. The rest was bad timing.'

'You mean Dad letting the cat out of the bag before you could say anything?' she jeered with a toss of her head.

'I had hoped for more time with you,' he told her, and she affected a look of disbelief, though his words played havoc with her senses.

'What on earth for? Your job was done,' she gibed, and Gray ground his teeth in irritation at her tone.

'Don't put yourself down.' His voice was suddenly serious. 'From an enticing young lady, you'd turned into a stunningly desirable woman.'

Her brows arched delicately as she heard that. 'The kind of woman you'd still like to get up close and personal with?'

'Very close. Very personal,' he admitted with just that husky edge to his voice which hinted at hidden fires and steaming hot passion.

It sent a powerful thrill of anticipation through her system, and it was all she could do to keep a cool head. 'Wow, you really know how to turn up the heat. I guess most women would be falling at your feet right about now?'

His lips twitched. 'Something like that.'

Shelby stared at him, anger starting a slow simmer inside her. She knew the game he was playing now. He wanted her and believed he could have her, if he played his cards right. Well, he was about to find out how wrong he was. She looked him squarely in the eye. 'Unluckily for you, I'm not most women.'

Gray folded his arms and studied her carefully. 'No, you're not,' he agreed, and there was an odd sense of satisfaction in the way he said it that puzzled her.

Walking over to him, she placed her palms against his cheeks, ignoring the prickle of heat which transmitted itself to her senses. 'I wouldn't get involved with you if you were the last man on earth,' she declared witheringly and stepped back with a shudder of distaste.

Gray's nostrils flared as he absorbed the insult, and an intense gleam danced in his eyes. 'That's your pride talking. Don't let it get in the way of what you want,' he advised seductively, and she raised her chin defiantly.

'Wanting and having are two different things. I freely admit to wanting you, and if I went along with your little plan I'm sure the experience would be…ravishing. However, I'd have to live with myself afterwards, and you wouldn't be worth the trouble,' she returned with feline intensity.

To her utter chagrin, he laughed and headed for the door. 'I shall have great pleasure in making you take that back. Once this is over, you'll be purring instead of spitting, little cat,' he added just before he disappeared from view.

Shelby's smile vanished abruptly. She stared at her hands, which still tingled from touching him, and wondered for a wild moment if she might still be dreaming, but she knew she wasn't. Gray really had just turned her world on its head.

He was attracted to her. Had been for a long time. Even

when he had been following her father's orders. That just made the sense of betrayal worse. Even his wanting of her came secondary to his work. Now, he thought, because she was still attracted to him, they could have an affair. Of all the nerve! Her blood was absolutely boiling. She was not going to fling herself into his arms, saying, Take me, I'm yours. Oh, no.

She loved him…though for the life of her she couldn't say why right now. There was no way she could overlook what he had done just because she wanted him physically! How dared he assume she was ripe for the picking? Some way, somehow, she was going to make him sorry for thinking that.

She kept this thought with her as she rinsed her dirty dishes in the sink and stacked them in the dishwasher. Then it was time to go.

Gray met her in the hallway and she couldn't help doing a double take when she saw him. Added to the black trousers and white T-shirt was a black jacket, from where he pulled a pair of designer sunglasses which he slipped on as she joined him. This was not the conservative businesslike Gray she knew at all. This Gray had wow factor! Good enough to eat and heart-trippingly sexy. Not that she was going to allow that to affect her decision about him.

She looked him up and down with a critical eye. 'Who would have thought there was a hunk hidden under all those grey business suits?' she said in mock amazement.

'You approve?'

'There's scarcely a red-blooded woman alive who wouldn't. You'll be beating them off with a stick,' Shelby added with wry honesty.

'But not you,' Gray surmised, holding up her car keys. 'You'll be driving. Try and keep your concentration on the road, not me.'

She shot him a haughty look as she took the keys and

went out ahead of him. 'Oh, please. You're not that irresistible.'

'Good. I'd be quite happy with fairly irresistible at the right time and place,' Gray returned, shutting the door behind them.

'And the right time and place would be?' she asked, calling the lift.

'I'll let you know when we reach it.'

Despite her determination not to respond, her nerves gave a tiny leap and she shivered. 'I'll be there, will I?'

'I'm certainly hoping so.' The lift arrived and they stepped inside.

Shelby laughed wryly. 'I'll say this for you, Gray. You're certainly not lacking in confidence.'

His responding laugh was soft and husky. 'It's the only way to get what you want.'

And he had decided he wanted her, she thought grimly. Well, they would see about that.

When the lift stopped, Gray put out a hand to prevent her from stepping out into the car park. He took an all-encompassing look around before taking her by the upper arm and urging her towards their parked cars.

'I feel foolish!' she exclaimed, though she kept her voice down instinctively.

His hold tightened fractionally. 'When you fall at my feet I don't want it to be because someone's taken a pot-shot at you!' he growled back sardonically.

'That isn't going to happen for any reason,' Shelby was quick to point out, using the remote to unlock the car doors as they walked.

'Put it this way, Red. You have to be alive to resist me. Let's keep it that way!'

She said nothing, merely climbed into her car and waited for him to join her. It was going to be a long day.

The journey out to her new client was uneventful, if you ignored the snarl of traffic. Once they were through it, Shelby made good time to the address she had been given. It was a very exclusive area. The understated aura of wealth oozed out from the parallel rows of detached houses. Turning into a manicured driveway, she parked the car before the door and turned to Gray, more in hope than expectation.

'I don't suppose you'll be staying in the car?'

'Not a chance. I need to be where you are,' he answered, just as she had expected.

Shelby reached for her briefcase and took from it a notebook and pen which she handed to him. 'OK, here are the rules. You take these and make notes. It doesn't matter what you write, just look efficient. Above all, don't say anything. Leave all the talking to me. Got it?'

With his sunglasses on she couldn't see his eyes, but the twist of his lips told her he was laughing at her again. 'Down to the last dotted i and crossed t.'

She looked at him doubtfully, but knew there was nothing she could do. 'This is going to be disastrous. I can feel it in my bones!' she exclaimed helplessly as she exited from the car. Climbing up a flight of steps, she took a steadying breath and rang the bell.

The door was opened by an elegantly dressed woman of that indeterminate age which could have been late thirties or early forties. 'Mrs Tyrwhit-Jones? How do you do? I'm…'

'Shelby Greer. I'm so pleased to meet you at last. Do call me Antonia,' Antonia Tyrwhit-Jones finished for her in a breathlessly excited voice. 'Do come in. I've heard so much about you. All my friends tell me how talented you are. I can't wait for you to do wonders with this old house.'

'I'll do my very best,' Shelby responded when she was allowed to get a word in. She could see the woman's eyes going beyond her to study Gray, who had followed them inside, and saw them widen as he drew her full attention. Much to Shelby's annoyance, they then turned decidedly predatory.

'Well, now, who might you be?' Antonia Tyrwhit-Jones asked with rather more than general interest. Fingering the pearls she wore at her throat, she looked Gray up and down with avaricious eyes.

Shelby experienced a violent wave of unadulterated dislike. Her expressed feelings notwithstanding, she took exception to the woman looking at Gray the way she was. In consequence, her reply was designed to put an end to the woman's interest.

'This is Serge. He'll be assisting me today. Taking notes, that sort of thing.' She introduced them.

Speculative eyes looked him over yet again as Antonia held her hand out. 'Pleased to meet you, Serge.' Gray removed his sunglasses and slipped them into his breast pocket, shook hands but said nothing. The other woman looked curiously at Shelby. 'I guess he's the strong silent type. He's very handsome, though. I just adore a man with muscles.'

Shelby pretty much decided there and then that she and Antonia Tyrwhit-Jones were not going to get along. However, she couldn't yet afford to turn away a prospective client. Luckily, there were other ways to skin a cat. Taking the other woman by the arm, she drew her aside, leaning in conversationally as she did so. 'Oh, I know. There's a catch, though. I'm afraid you're not his type.'

Automatically the woman raised a hand to her bleached blonde hair. 'Not blondes?'

Shelby gave her a woman to woman look. 'Not the right sex,' she declared in a loud whisper, and caught the sound of a strangled protest from behind her.

Her client was suitably deflated and looked at Gray with

a shake of her head. 'It can't be true. What a waste! Oh, well, never mind. Now tell me, Shelby, would you like to look at the upstairs rooms first or the downstairs? Or we could have some coffee?'

Having successfully diverted the other woman, Shelby smiled brightly. 'The upstairs rooms first, I think, Antonia. Then I'll make my way down. We can discuss your requirements and any ideas I come up with over coffee later. I like to get an overall feel of the place first.'

'Just as you like. I'm sure you know best,' she conceded, though, as the other woman led the way upstairs, Shelby had the feeling Antonia Thyrwit-Jones was not going to be an easy woman to work with.

Having given them a brief tour of the layout, during which she sent Gray more than one wistful glance, Antonia finally left them alone in the main bedroom, departing with a waggle of her fingers. Shelby let her breath out in a whoosh as she relaxed. The feeling lasted for maybe five seconds, then Gray narrowed his eyes on her.

'Serge?' he queried in disgust, and Shelby couldn't help bursting into a fit of giggles.

She hid her face behind her hands. 'I had to do something. I think she was about to jump your bones.'

'Well, she isn't going to do that now, is she? Not when you told her I wasn't interested in women,' he growled, moving towards her in a purposeful manner.

In the interest of self-preservation Shelby began to back away. 'Take it easy, Gray. It was just a joke!'

'Joke? Do you see me laughing?' he demanded in a tone that set her nerves quivering.

Shelby continued to retreat as he advanced. 'Where's your sense of humour?'

Teeth flashed whitely as he grinned menacingly. 'Lost under a powerful desire to strangle you!'

'Would it help if I apologised?' Shelby asked, just as the

back of her knees came in contact with the bed and, unable to prevent it, she sat down abruptly.

'It wouldn't help if you grovelled from here to doomsday,' he growled, hovering over her so that she fell backwards on to the covers. 'You're going to be sorry you said that, Red.'

Heart pounding, Shelby stared up at him. 'What are you going to do?' she asked breathlessly, moistening her lips with the tip of her tongue. This morning it had been a purely nervous response and she had seen the result. Now she used it as a diversionary tactic, and it worked like a dream.

Gray froze, closing his eyes as he took in a deep breath. 'You had to do it, didn't you?'

Shelby smothered a giggle and blinked, feigning ignorance. 'What?'

Opening his eyes, he speared her on the end of a blue gaze. 'That sexy little trick with your tongue.'

It was highly erotic, lying on the bed with him looming over her, and her breathing went awry as her senses responded to his closeness. 'You mean this?' she asked, doing it again and catching the faint sound of a groan issuing from him. 'It's a nervous gesture.'

'It's damned distracting. That's what it is, you little tease!' Gray corrected as he straightened up and moved away from her.

Sitting up again, hiding an urge to smile, Shelby smoothed down her hair. First round to her. 'I had no idea I could put you off your stride just by licking my lips.' Now that she did, she wondered how she could use it to her advantage.

'Believe me, Red, there are a lot of things you don't know you can do,' he informed her cryptically and, not surprisingly, she was intrigued by the notion. There was more?

'What things?' she wanted to know, but Gray had said all he was going to. When it came to teasing, he had his own methods. Disappointment had her stomach sinking. 'You can't just leave it there.' She wanted to know what powers she had that could be used against him.

He stared at her, a smile slowly curving his lips. 'I have left it there. You can't expect me to do all your work for you.'

Which meant she was going to have to go by trial and error. That could turn out to be hazardous, but he left her no choice. 'I hate it when you say things like that!' she complained with a decided sniff of displeasure. Which was water off a duck's back to Gray, who simply stood there, arms crossed and an inscrutable smile on his face.

'The trouble with you is you've led a pampered lifestyle,' he told her in the next breath, and Shelby took instant exception.

'I've never been pampered. Indulged from time to time, but never pampered,' she corrected him whilst she opened her briefcase and took out a retractable tape measure.

'You mean none of the men you've dated have ever bought you things?' Gray wanted to know, watching her take measurements with speed and efficiency.

Shelby shook her head. 'I discouraged it. Men who buy you things tend to think they own you,' she explained. 'Make yourself useful and take a note of these dimensions,' she went on, reeling off the figures she had, then going on to add more.

Gray glanced up from the pad he was writing on. 'Some men never learn that you have to let a wild thing have room to breathe and roam. That way they'll come to you of their own accord.'

She looked at him in surprise, having been called many things but never that. 'You think I'm wild? I think I'm insulted.'

He laughed. 'Don't be. You're not wild, but you have spirit. Reining you in would be a crime.'

To her surprise, his words caused a bubbly sensation in her stomach and she pressed a hand over it to settle it down. She couldn't let him see he had touched a nerve. 'So, hypothetically speaking, what you're saying is this. If we were married, you wouldn't tie me down?' she asked lightly.

'Don't get me wrong. I'm male enough to want to make certain you know you're mine but, having done that, you would have all the freedom you craved,' he confirmed, then laughed. 'Realistically, of course, you and I are about as close to getting married as the earth is from the moon.'

Even though it was entirely what she would expect him to say, it cut her to the quick. 'Just as well, as I want nothing to do with you, one way or the other,' Shelby shot back mockingly, hiding her wounds. She turned to the window she had been sizing up.

'If ever there were two people not meant for each other, we're them,' Gray mused, and she glanced over her shoulder.

'Absolutely. Any relationship requires trust, and you've already proved I can't trust you,' she informed him with a frosty smile, turning back to the job in hand.

It was a downright shame, because she knew that, given the chance, she could make him happy. However, he had made it more than clear that what he wanted from her had nothing to do with love. Marriage was not even a remote possibility. Which brought his interest down to pure old fashioned sex. Which she had nothing against, and had an idea that with him it would be fantastic. Her heart, though, would still hunger. She hadn't ever imagined that she would be one to suffer from unrequited love. Life had a way of playing tricks on a person.

'We'd better get on or Antonia will be back. I don't think

I could bear to see her sending you any more disappointed glances.'

Gray made a growling sound in his throat. 'Hell, no. The woman makes me nervous.'

Shelby laughed with genuine amusement. 'Now that I don't believe!'

'Trust me, Red, there's a look in her eye that says she'd like to try and return me to the straight and narrow. You might have to pull her off me,' he said, very much tongue-in-cheek.

She glanced back over her shoulder again. 'Don't worry. I'll protect you. I didn't like the way she was looking at you, anyway.'

One eyebrow quirked. 'I noticed. Why is that?'

She hadn't allowed for the question, but the answer was easy. 'Why? Because you're off limits for the duration, remember?' Shelby declared dryly. 'I'm not suffering this thing on my own!'

'Shame. I thought you might have being going to tell me she was poaching on your preserve,' he said, shooting her a rakish look.

Shelby very nearly cut her finger as the steel tape shot back into its holder. 'Ouch!' she gasped, sucking the damaged digit. 'You've got to be kidding!' she exclaimed derisively.

Gray's lips twitched and there was a wicked light in his eyes. 'It was just a thought.'

She shook her head sadly. 'Well, you can keep those kind of thoughts to yourself in future. You're only here because of this ridiculous threat. It changes nothing between us. You're still a rat. I still despise you, and probably will till the day I die. Which, as you are here to make sure that doesn't happen too soon, leaves years of hating ahead of me.'

Gray heard her out, then had the gall to smile. 'If you

put as much passion into making love with me as you do into despising me, we're in for interesting times. OK, then, what's next?'

Shelby would dearly have liked to throw something at him, but in a client's house it was out of the question. So she satisfied herself by turning her back on him. Lord, let this be over soon, she prayed, because the way things were going she wasn't going to come out of it unscathed!

CHAPTER FOUR

SHELBY prepared for the charity dinner with extra-special care. Although it wasn't the way she had expected to spend the evening, she was going to be with Gray. That being the case, she was determined to look her best. Actually, her unspoken plan was to knock him totally off balance. She wanted him to see what he was missing. What he was never going to have.

She had already bought a new dress for the occasion before the current situation had occurred. It was a shimmering affair in shades of turquoise and green, with tiny straps to hold it up, and was so light she barely felt as if she had it on. Her reflection in the mirror showed her an elegant young woman with perfect make-up, her red hair piled on top of her head in an ageless and very feminine style. A matching stole draped across her neck and over each shoulder, and sandals and evening purse completed the ensemble.

Shelby thought she looked good, but what would Gray think? Would he be smitten? Not that she seriously wanted him to be. She meant what she had said this morning. However, there was nothing wrong in taunting him. That he did deserve. In spades.

A sharp knock on her bedroom door caused her to turn her head quickly.

'Taxi's waiting downstairs,' Gray called out, and her heart upped its beat all of a sudden.

'I'll be there in a second,' she answered, and pressed a hand over her stomach. Suddenly she felt incredibly nervous. Even her palms felt moist, and she rubbed them on her thighs to dry them. She was crazy! All this anxiety was because she wanted him to like what he saw. More than that, she wanted him to want what he saw. That way, when she rebuffed his advances, the laugh would be on him. And if that wasn't nice of her, too bad. He had been laughing at her for too long.

Knowing that she had taken all the time she could, Shelby took a steadying breath and left the room. In her lounge, Gray was waiting by the fireplace, his hands hidden in the trouser pockets of his dress suit. She must have made some sound, for he glanced round, his eyes automatically running over her. Hers did the same to him, and her heart turned over. He looked—magnificent.

Then her gaze left his clothes and travelled to his face, and there in his eyes she saw what she had long been hoping to see, and it very nearly caused her heart to stop. As their gazes locked she saw the unmistakable heat and flames of a powerful desire. He wanted her. Even though she had been hoping to see it, it sent shock waves rippling along her nerves, heightening her senses, so that she could feel an electric intensity in the air between them.

'Stunning,' Gray declared simply, never taking his eyes off her.

'Back at you,' Shelby responded, holding his gaze and feeling the temperature rise as her blood heated up.

'If it was your plan to make it difficult for me to keep my hands off you, you've succeeded,' he added in that kind of male growl guaranteed to set her nerves fluttering expectantly.

Shelby hastily reminded herself she was not supposed to get caught up in the moment, and ran a hand from her waist to her hip. 'I'm glad you like it.'

He walked towards her slowly. 'I'm going to have my work cut out keeping my mind on my job tonight.'

She was pleased she had achieved her first objective and

knocked him off balance this way. Of course, she hadn't meant to get knocked off balance herself in the process. 'I thought I was your job, and your plan was to keep an eye on me,' she reminded him, her breath hitching in her throat as he stopped mere inches away. Maybe this was not going to be as easy as she'd thought. She hadn't taken the strength of her own responses into account.

'By not looking at you. How can I watch your back if I'm watching your front?' he asked her in that same seductive growl.

He was good at this. She had to remind herself that he was the enemy here. Taking a deep breath, she regained some of her equilibrium. 'Seems like you have a problem. Let me solve it for you. Take the evening off. I promise not to tell,' she added in a confidential whisper.

He shook his head regretfully. 'No can do, sweetheart. I promised your father I'd take care of you.'

The words were all she needed to get her feet back on the ground and return her pulse to normal. She was just a job to him tonight. He was under orders, and she knew how single-minded he was about obeying her father's wishes. Her smile faded.

'Ah, yes, the magic words. You promised Dad. Where would you be without them? When he says jump, your only response is to ask how high!' she responded scathingly, turning towards the front door.

'In respect of you, certainly. You're a responsibility I don't take lightly,' Gray informed her with some impatience as they left the flat and took the lift down to the lobby.

Shelby looked at him mockingly. 'Sounds to me like the job's getting to you,' she taunted, but he merely shrugged the comment off.

'I'll survive. Cold showers usually help. It won't be the first one I've taken because of you, Red,' he added dryly.

Her brows rose in genuine surprise. 'I had no idea.'

One eyebrow quirked her way. 'A man has to have some secrets.'

'So why are you telling me?'

Walking through the lobby, Gray took hold of her arm as they approached the outside door. His steps slowed as he took an all encompassing look round before they passed outside. 'Because now you're intrigued,' he told her, holding open the door of the taxi, following her in seconds later. Giving the directions to the driver, he sat back and glanced at her. 'Women who are intrigued by a man come back for more,' he explained and she tutted reprovingly.

'Said with typical male arrogance. Anyway, should you be revealing your strategy like this?' she asked, frowning as he turned in his seat to study the road behind them. Clearly satisfied with what he saw, he turned back and gave her a sardonic look.

'You already know the best tricks, Red. You use them all the time yourself,' he shot back.

It was true. However, she had never actually tried any of her repertoire on him. She might have, had she known then what she knew now. When he had taken the initiative later she had simply followed her heart. He must be a hell of a poker player because she hadn't got even the smallest inkling that in the first instance he had been attracted and in the second that it was all a ploy. Which had been his intention, and it was something she would do well to remember.

'Why did you always hide this wild attraction you want me to believe you always felt for me?' she asked out of curiosity.

'You're the boss's daughter. Only a fool would mess with that situation,' he responded dryly. She got his point, except for one thing.

'I'm still the boss's daughter,' Shelby pointed out, making him grin.

'True, but you're not eighteen any longer. You're an independent woman.'

'And, as you can't have the woman you really want, you'll make do with what's available?' she rejoined sardonically and received a long cool look for her pains.

'Let's leave her out of this, shall we?' Gray suggested in a voice that said she'd be wise to heed his warning. 'Besides, getting involved with you could hardly be called 'making do',' he added with wry laughter, and took yet another look out the rear window.

Shelby rolled her eyes heavenwards. 'I wish you wouldn't keep doing that. It's driving me crazy!' she complained in mild exasperation.

'Stop complaining or I'll strangle you myself,' Gray threatened lightly.

'Come on, Gray, admit it,' Shelby encouraged, twisting to face him. 'You don't really think somebody is going to shoot at me from a passing car any more than I do.'

She was expecting a grin but he remained serious. 'Not in this country, but we could be followed. An opportunist needs only seconds to act. I don't intend to give him the chance.'

Shelby couldn't help but glance out the rear window herself. 'Are we being followed?' she asked nervously, wondering how she would recognise if they were.

'No, so you can sit back and relax. All you need worry about right now is if your lipstick is still on. Leave the rest to me.'

She subsided back into her seat and sent him a stony glare. 'Don't be so damned patronising. I have a brain, you know.'

'Now would be a good time to start using it, then,' Gray commanded caustically, setting her back up instantly.

'You know what I think? This love of your life could see what you were like, and got out whilst the going was good!' she gibed, and got his full attention. The chill in his eyes was awesome.

'Don't go there, Red. I won't warn you a third time,' he said in a soft voice that struck as hard as steel.

After holding his gaze for a moment, Shelby looked away, swallowing a lump in her throat. She didn't know why she was being so catty about this unknown woman. Which was a lie, because of course she knew. The woman had something she would never possess. His heart. It hurt, proving, if proof were necessary, that she cared. Loved him beyond reason, for reason would have told her to hate him a long time ago. Deciding she was a hopeless case, she sighed heavily.

The remainder of the fairly short journey passed in uncomfortable silence and if it annoyed her that Gray regularly checked the road she wisely kept it to herself.

The hall housing the charity function was ablaze with lights and they joined the crowd mounting the steps, Gray taking a firm hold of her arm and keeping her close beside him. For the first time Shelby actually felt vulnerable for a moment. Her back was a clear target to anyone watching for her, and she was glad when they finally managed to get inside the relative safety of the foyer. So much for her intention not to buy into the situation.

Thankfully, the instant they entered the ballroom she was greeted by numerous friends and acquaintances, and the moment passed off. Most of her friends were already gathered at their assigned table and, seeing the speculation when they saw the man accompanying her, she swiftly introduced Gray, though she fell shy of calling him her date.

'How is it I can never find anyone who looks like you?' her friend Nadia despaired as she shook hands. 'Are you married?'

'Nadia!' everyone exclaimed at once amidst the general laughter.

'How else am I to know?' Nadia went on, unabashed.

Gray laughed softly. 'No, but I'm afraid I'm spoken for,' he told her, giving Shelby a sizzling look at the same time, which sent goose-bumps all over her, even as she tensed at the message he had given out. Having taken her by surprise, she couldn't gainsay him. They were, for tonight at least, an item. Damn him!

Nadia sighed wistfully. 'Shelby has all the luck. When she came in positively glowing I knew you were someone special.'

Shelby's nerves performed a wild lurch. Had she been glowing? She couldn't look to Gray for help, for he had put her in this unenviable situation. All she could do was throw her weight behind it and make him pay later.

'I can't help it. He's absolutely fabulous,' she declared brightly, squeezing Gray's arm and reaching up to plant a kiss on his cheek. It was as well she didn't have to say anything else, for her lips were tingling from the unexpected pleasure and couldn't have formed words anyway.

'I know what you mean. I'd be glowing if I had a man like that holding my arm!' Nadia exclaimed with a wicked roll of her eyes and everyone laughed again.

The next few minutes were taken up with shaking hands and greeting everyone, but finally they gained a breathing space.

'What are you playing at?' Shelby hissed at him once they were seated and the teasing had passed on to somebody else.

'I thought it best to make out we were an item,' Gray responded, shooting her a quizzical look. 'As you left the door open, I decided to get in first, remembering the last introduction you made,' he added dryly.

That brought a warm glow to her cheeks. 'You'd annoyed me,' she excused herself, and he smiled.

'I annoy you a lot. Maybe if you worked with me, instead of against me, we could avoid these little mishaps,' he suggested, and she knew he was laughing at her.

'Thanks for nothing. You realise they're going to be asking questions about you for ever,' Shelby returned dryly, then frowned as she saw the mark of her kiss on his cheek. 'Oops, it looks like I've branded you. Do you have a handkerchief?' He produced one from his pocket, which she shook out and deftly removed the lipstick before handing it back. 'There you are. All gone,' she declared, then caught him watching her and raised her brows questioningly. 'What is it?'

'I know what your friend meant about you glowing. There's something about you tonight that's quite intoxicating.'

Her heart did another of its spectacular flip-flops and she momentarily lost her breath even though she knew it was part of the role he was playing tonight. 'You can stop now. Nobody's watching,' she told him, only to receive a swift, almost invisible, shake of the head.

'Actually, darling, we're being observed by people on neighbouring tables, so you might want to say something nice for a change,' he corrected her assumption under his breath.

The endearment set her heart trotting, but she realised why he had said it when a surreptitious glance around proved he was right. They were being watched. There was to be no relief tonight, it seemed. She had to play the role he had given her to the hilt. To which end she produced a flirtatious smile.

'If I might say so, you're looking quite sizzling yourself.'

Gray rubbed the side of his nose, his expression wry. 'I don't believe I've ever been told I sizzle before.'

She gave a tiny shrug, her body leaning towards him slightly. 'Believe me, you do. It's very sexy.'

Blue eyes danced at her comment and his lips twitched. 'You're very good at this.'

Shelby trailed her fingers along his arm. 'So are you. Aren't we a pair? We're gold medal class in flirtation, but when it comes to relationships we're pushed to come in last!'

Gray captured her hand and turned it over, surveying the lines engraved there. 'Are you still searching for Mr Right?'

A tiny ache settled about her heart as she watched the only man for her trace his finger over her palm. 'I think, when his ship came in, I was at the airport,' she breezed lightly, making a joke of it so it wouldn't hurt too much. Picking up her evening bag, she stood up. 'I need to use the powder room.'

Immediately Gray rose too. 'OK, let's go.'

Unable to say anything with her friends looking on, she had to wait until they were in the foyer again before attempting to pull her arm free of his hand. 'There's no need to go with me. I know the way!' she protested, to no avail.

'Sorry, Red, you know the score. Where you go, I go.'

Shock tore through her as she realised what he was saying. 'You can't possibly come into the ladies' room with me!' she argued, finding it hard to keep her voice down so as not to draw unwanted attention.

'Want to bet?' he shot back in grim amusement, and Shelby came to an abrupt halt outside the powder room door.

'You can't.'

'It's a risk I'm prepared to take,' he informed her blithely, taking charge of the situation, pushing open the door and walking in, tugging her in his wake.

The three ladies in possession of the outer room looked up in surprise.

Gray turned on the charm. 'Excuse me, ladies, but this young woman thought she saw something scuttling about in here, and I've come to check it out. If you could just step outside for a moment, I promise not to keep you more than a few minutes. Is there anyone in the other room?'

The three ladies, who had gathered up their belongings in haste at the mention of scuttling, made for the door he held open.

'It's empty,' one of the women said, answering his question, and received the full force of his dashing smile.

'Thank you for your co-operation,' he told them, closing the door and shooting the lock.

Shelby pressed her palms to cheeks burning red with mortification. 'I can't believe you just did that!' she wailed. 'I've never been so embarrassed in my life!'

'Then you've led a sheltered existence,' Gray retorted, entering the other room, which was empty as he had been told, but checking out each stall to make sure. Reappearing, he stepped away from the doorway. 'It's OK, you can go in there now,' he informed her, and she stared at him, totally stunned.

'You couldn't seriously have thought someone would be hiding in there,' she protested, only to see him shake his head.

'No, as it happens. However, you'll think twice before you ever cast aspersions on my manhood again,' Gray revealed, eyes starting to twinkle triumphantly as he saw understanding dawn on her face.

'You...you...!' she exclaimed, hands balling into angry fists. 'You did this just to get your own back for this morning? What a mean, nasty, horrible...'

A rat-tat on the door interrupted her harangue.

'People are getting impatient,' Gray reminded her, and she drew in a deep breath.

'Thank you, but I no longer wish to go,' she informed

him in a frosty tone, whereupon he walked to the door and opened it.

'Sorry, ladies. Everything is fine; the young lady was imagining things,' he apologised to the small crowd waiting outside.

Shelby had to run the gauntlet of speculative eyes yet again and wished the floor would open up and swallow her.

'That was a rotten trick,' she told him in an aggrieved voice.

'Now you know how I felt,' was all he said in response.

Maybe, but she wasn't about to admit it after what he had just done. 'I may never forgive you.'

He had the gall to laugh. 'Never is a long time. Even you wouldn't hold a grudge quite that long,' he pointed out sardonically, making Shelby grind her teeth.

'I'll give it a damned good try,' she countered, and caught a flash of his grin.

'Now that I do believe.'

She really did hate him sometimes. 'You're impossible.'

'And you're stunningly beautiful when you're angry,' Gray returned smoothly, stealing her thunder and twisting her heartstrings.

'What...? I mean...stop trying to change the subject. I'm mad at you and I want to stay mad,' Shelby harangued him, though her anger had suddenly vanished like magic.

They had, by this time, returned to their table, and Gray held her chair out for her. She sat down but, before moving away, Gray bent down in an intimate gesture and nuzzled her ear.

'Stay as mad as you like, sweetheart. I wouldn't stop you for the world,' he murmured, sending tingles down her spine and curling her toes.

There was no getting away from it, she was a hopeless case where he was concerned, which gave him a heck of a weapon to use against her. The situation this evening gave him the opportunity to use a lot of unfair tactics. If she wanted to compete, she was going to have to take a leaf out of his book.

The chance to do so came along much sooner than she had expected. Having waived the first course of soup, Shelby was quite ready to tuck in to the main course when it was put before her—until she had a whimsical thought.

'Aren't you forgetting something?' she asked Gray, with her knife and fork poised over her plate. He quirked a questioning eyebrow in her direction. 'This food could be poisoned.'

He looked naturally dubious. 'The plate came along with all the others.'

'I know,' she whispered back. 'But the waiter could be in the employ of this nasty individual, and sprinkled poison on my plate. I need an official food taster, and you're it.' Hiding a grin, she cut off a small wedge of meat, speared it on her fork and held it out to him. 'Open up!'

With a resigned sigh, Gray abandoned his cutlery and reached for the fork. 'You realise you're messing with the wrong man,' he growled, placing his hand over hers and making it impossible for her to pull free. He helped her to put the small morsel in his mouth, and all the time his eyes never left hers.

The bottom fell out of her stomach as he savoured the meat and she couldn't look away. It was one of the most intensely sensual moments she had ever experienced sitting at a dinner table, and it had her heart pounding, sending her blood pulsing thickly through her veins. Over in seconds, she knew she would never forget it.

'Mmm, delicious,' Gray declared huskily, eyes hot and sultry. 'Do you want me to try the potatoes?'

Shelby didn't think her system could withstand it. She cleared her throat. 'No, thank you, that will be quite suf-

ficient.' Reaching for her glass with a faintly trembling
hand, she took a much needed sip of wine.

Of course, every mouthful she took after that carried with
it the memory of watching Gray eat, knowing it hadn't been
food he was savouring but herself. There were some things,
she decided, that shouldn't be tried in mixed company.
Taunting him was one of them.

The evening wore on. Speeches followed the meal, the
organisers thanking everyone for supporting the charity so
generously. Afterwards the floor was cleared for dancing to
a live band, and everyone was left to enjoy themselves as
they wished. Much chatter and laughter bubbled round their
table, but eventually couples started to drift on to the floor
to dance.

After a few minutes, Gray held out his hand. 'Let's
dance,' he suggested, and Shelby's brows arched in surprise. It wasn't that she didn't want to, merely that she
hadn't expected he would.

'Are you sure?' she queried, keeping her voice low so
as not to be overheard.

'It would look odd not to,' he confirmed, getting to his
feet, hand still outstretched.

Which left her with little choice other than to put her
hand in his and let him help her up. He was quite right, it
would look odd. Having given the impression they were a
new item, then getting 'closer' on the dance floor would be
the natural thing to do. Whilst part of her saw danger signals, there was a stronger part that wanted to get close to
him, with a good reason for doing so. Something that had
nothing to do with her attraction to him, but was merely
playing the game.

Shelby allowed him to lead her through the tables to the
dance floor, where he neatly turned her into his arms as
they joined the circling mass. She hadn't known what to
expect, and it was a curious sensation. Gray was playing it

strictly by the book, holding her with the correct distance between them, and after a while she realised that that was not what she wanted at all.

It was like a peculiar form of torture where she was being tantalised by his nearness, her senses awakening to the promise of unexpected delights, but not getting them. Though it would not help her declared intention of not falling into his arms, she couldn't help herself. She wanted to be closer, to experience their bodies touching. She wanted his arms around her, for goodness' sake, and nothing less would do. So when they were bumped the next time she acted swiftly, shifting the hand which was resting on his shoulder and sliding it around his neck, her fingers curling into the silky strands of his hair. At the same time her body came to rest against his, delighting in the feel of his powerful torso. Holding her breath, she waited for Gray's reaction.

After the briefest hesitation his hand which had been on her waist found its way round to her back, settled there and began sending out a wave of heat. Her blood sang, whilst her heart stepped up its rhythm. Lord, what a fool she was to think she could deny herself this way. This was what she had longed for and, without a thought, she lowered her head and rested it on his shoulder.

'Not going to sleep on me, are you, Red?' Gray asked a short while later and, although the tone was light, she could hear a thickness in his voice which told her he was far from being unaffected.

Sleeping had never been further from her mind. Her body was too alive for that and so, she could tell, was his. 'Just setting the scene,' she sighed, rubbing her cheek against the soft fabric of his suit and catching the powerful scent of maleness mixed with cologne. Lord, but he smelt good!

Now, as they slowly circled the floor, their bodies brushed against each other with every slow movement and the effect was electric. It was exactly how she had always dreamed it would be, and she was intoxicated by the sensations. It was glorious, and she wanted to stay in his arms for ever.

'Are you planning to seduce me right here, by any chance?' Gray queried, catching his breath as another bump pressed them closer together and set off sparks.

Still lost in the mood, Shelby laughed softly. 'We'd never be allowed through the doors again,' she said wryly, her fingers playing with his hair.

'Cut it out, Red!' he commanded in the next breath, and she tipped her head up so that she could see him looking down at her.

'I thought you liked women running their fingers through your hair,' she breathed huskily, and she was fascinated to hear him groan and close his eyes for an instant.

'In private, not in the middle of a dance floor.'

She bit her lip but her eyes were sparkling and she received full strength the powerful force of his blue eyes, with the banked fires of desire in their depths. 'I think I'd better stop,' she capitulated, reluctantly bringing herself out of the dream she had been in, back to the here and now.

'You might want to remember for next time that playing with fire can be dangerous,' Gray returned dryly.

With a sharp jolt to her nerves, Shelby knew she had been playing with fire and she was sending messages she had no intention of backing up. 'There won't be a next time,' she insisted, knowing she had been a fool to indulge herself.

Now it was his turn to laugh. 'The way we respond to each other, how can you say no?'

'Because this was just for show. Nothing's changed between us, Gray,' she reminded him coolly. 'I'm not going to get involved with you, no matter how good it feels.'

'Because of the past? Let it go, Red. You won't be

sorry,' Gray argued persuasively, and there was a tiny part of her that was tempted. However, the larger part remembered the hurt of betrayal and could not forgive.

Just at that moment the song came to an end and, in the pause before the next began, Shelby stepped away from him.

'Perhaps we ought to sit this one out?' she suggested, which brought forth the wolfish smile which always managed to send shivers up her spine.

'Oh, I think we can survive another, providing you keep your hands to yourself,' he countered, eyes glittering roguishly as he neatly pulled her back into his arms again and started moving before she could argue.

Had the situation not been so public she would have fought free even if it did cause a scene, but she could not do so here. So she resigned herself to sweating it out. It wasn't easy. Though Shelby kept her hands to herself, Gray didn't. The hand he settled on her back began to make lazy and highly sensuous forays up and down her spine.

'Hmm, this is nice,' he murmured a few minutes later.

It was more than nice. It was the nearest thing to heaven she'd ever experienced. 'You do realise you're not playing fair?' she complained, her voice tense with the effort to remain cool-headed whilst her senses were under siege.

'Fair is for children. The battle between us isn't about winning or losing.'

That was a surprise. She was under the impression that was exactly what it was. 'What is it about, then?'

'It's all about finding reasonable terms for surrender,' Gray explained huskily and said no more, leaving her to wonder if there ever could be such a thing.

This time when the music ended they returned to the table, which was once again full of chattering people. Later, a photographer appeared and took snaps of them all, leaving copies on the table for them to take if they wanted.

Shelby feigned disinterest in the one of her and Gray, but when she went in search of it later before they left, it was gone. Disappointed, she went to join Gray, who had called for a taxi.

Gray's words came back to her then. Reasonable terms for surrender, she mused to herself as the cab whisked them homewards. She had never considered their relationship from that angle. Could she live with that? Could she ignore the past and simply start from now? She yawned, thoughts blurring, and had no idea she had dropped off to sleep until she was gently shaken awake and realised her head was resting on Gray's shoulder.

'Sorry,' she apologised, stifling a yawn.

'You're out on your feet, Red. Do you want me to carry you?' he offered as he helped her out of the car.

She shook her head. 'I can manage. Besides, you need to keep your hands free in order to repel attackers,' she reminded him pertly, then spoilt everything by stumbling over a flagstone.

Gray nimbly swung her up into his arms, ignoring her protest. 'I promise to drop you if the need arises.'

They made it to her floor with little trouble. Gray set her down long enough to open the door, then he picked her up again, shut the door with his foot on the way in and strode to her bedroom, where he gently set her down on her bed.

'Do you need any help undressing?'

'That I can do.'

He smiled wryly. 'OK. You know where I am if you need me.'

'My hero!' she sighed, and he went out laughing softly.

Shelby made one last effort to wash off her make-up and slip into her nightdress, then she collapsed into her bed with a sigh of pleasure. It had been an odd sort of day, with surprising highs. She could hear Gray moving about, making sure everything was secure, but after a while even he grew silent.

As sleep drew ever closer, she marvelled at the knowledge that she was actually contemplating the possibility of maybe having an affair with the man. It hardly seemed possible, and yet it was true. What Gray had said back there on the dance floor made a weird kind of sense. Reasonable terms for surrender, he had said, and Lord, how she wanted to do that. She fought on because he had hurt her so badly. He didn't know that, of course. He thought she was merely holding a grudge. So she could back down and have what she wanted, without him ever knowing there was more to it. If she wanted. Not that she had to decide yet. Nothing was going to happen until all this was over. She could think about it some more. Thinking didn't commit her to anything.

Yawning widely, she turned on to her side, and in seconds sleep finally claimed her.

CHAPTER FIVE

THE following day was hectic from the word go. Unless Shelby had an early appointment with a client, she always called in to her office every morning. Currently she had two projects on the go, one of which was about halfway along and the other almost completed. With a growing waiting-list, she employed a workforce of three women whom she could trust to work to her plans, but she checked in every day or so to see how the jobs were progressing, and because she loved doing the hands-on work herself.

Her assistant, Paula, was overseeing the final details at their first port of call and ,when Shelby walked in, was hanging curtains.

'Oh, wow! They look great, Paula. I'm glad we went with that pattern,' she declared with satisfaction.

Coming to join Shelby and the ever attendant Gray, who had followed her in, Paula nodded. 'Sets it all off nicely,' she agreed, eyes flickering to her boss's companion with patent curiosity.

'Now, if only we could get those vases for the fireplace, we'd be finished,' Shelby sighed, turning to evaluate the unadorned hearth.

'What's wrong with it as it is?' Gray asked the obvious question and found himself being surveyed like an alien by the two women.

Shelby shook her head sadly. 'Philistine! Paula, this is Gray, an old friend,' she introduced him, having decided it was the only thing she could call him to the people who worked for her. 'He'll be keeping me company for a few days. Gray, meet Paula, my indispensable right hand.'

They shook hands, Paula grinning at his confused expression. 'A good designer knows when the job is finished. All this needs is the vases, and that will be it. Perfection. Until then...'

'Don't ask stupid questions,' Shelby finished for her, having circled the room and taken in all the changes since her last visit. 'Gray can't help it. I think he was dropped on his head as a baby,' she added, shooting a mocking glance his way.

Gray slipped his hands into the pockets of his jeans. He had taken his lead from Shelby, who had chosen to wear jeans and a stripy shirt today. 'She'll be sorry she said that later.'

Paula laughed. 'Oh, I see. You're *that* kind of old friend.'

That drew Shelby's attention away from the nearby table lamp. 'Certainly not. He's a friend, full stop,' she denied instantly, sending him a warning glare. Which he promptly ignored.

'That wasn't the impression I got when I carried you to bed last night,' Gray countered smoothly, and her lips parted on a tiny gasp.

'Don't listen to him, Paula, he's making it all up,' she advised the other woman, but Gray simply quirked a lazy eyebrow at her and flashed a smile.

'Calm down, Red. It would have to come out in the end that we're living together,' he went on soothingly, making her blood boil even more.

'Don't you dare tell me to calm down!' Shelby exclaimed wrathfully. What was he playing at?

Paula glanced from one to the other and coughed. 'Um, I think I'll go make us some tea. You two clearly have other things to discuss,' she declared and beat a hasty retreat.

The instant she was gone, Shelby rounded on Gray.

'What on earth do you think you're doing?' she demanded to know.

'I decided that the idea of our being an item would probably work best with your staff. Seeing me here constantly wouldn't seem odd,' he told her reasonably, but Shelby didn't feel mollified.

'You could have at least discussed it with me first! I was happy with you merely being a friend,' she snapped back, breast heaving with anger at his arrogance.

Something glittered in his eyes. 'But we're not friends, Red. We're more than that,' he corrected her in a smoky kind of voice that teased her senses.

Her own eyes narrowed. 'We're not the lovers you want everyone to think we are!' Shelby was so mad she could spit nails.

To add to her irritation, he merely shrugged. 'It's too late now. Nobody will believe you if you try to take it back. You're just going to have to live with it.'

There was, she noted, a certain smug satisfaction in the way he said it, and if there had been a poker on the hearth she might well have used it where it would do most good. However, there wasn't, so she was forced to take a deep steadying breath. He was right, there was nothing she could do, but she didn't like it, and she didn't like him for doing it.

'One of these days you're going to get your comeuppance, Gray Compton, and I only hope I'm there to see it!' she vowed with heartfelt dislike.

Gray's lips twisted wryly. 'If there's any justice in this world, we'll both get our just deserts one day.'

'We can but live in hope,' she added sourly, and he laughed.

'I like the room, by the way. It's very relaxing,' Gray complimented and Shelby took another deep breath and regained her objectivity.

'Thank you. That's exactly what we were aiming for,' she said, unable to prevent her heart swelling rather more than was necessary at the compliment. Though she knew it was ridiculous, she realised she wanted him to like what she did. Wanted him to be proud of her. Loving someone did that to a person. Which once again emphasised just what a hopeless case she was. She couldn't keep her emotions balanced from one moment to the next.

After chatting with Paula for some time, Shelby and Gray finally departed and headed for the remaining project. This commission was to bring a new look to an upmarket apartment. Plasterers, carpenters and electricians had all done their job and now it was up to Shelby and her assistants, Jacquie and Sue, to add the distinctive touch that would make it a Shelby Greer design.

As soon as they arrived, Shelby slipped into overalls to protect her clothes. The lounge floor was covered by cloths and in the centre were pots of paint, trays, rollers and brushes. She went to these and picked up various items plus a can of paint, which she handed to Gray with a winsome smile.

'Since we'll be here for a while, you might as well make yourself useful. You do know how to use a roller, don't you?'

'You actually trust me not to make a mistake?'

She gave him a look. 'Do I have idiot written across my forehead? You'll be applying base coat. Even you can't make a mess of that.'

He grinned wryly. 'I knew there had to be a catch. Where do I start?'

'At the door. Go all the way round the room till you get back to it. I'd offer you some overalls, but we don't have anything in your size,' Shelby said, grinning back at him. 'Have fun.'

She left him to it and went off to make preparations in

another room. When she glanced in some time later, Gray had rolled up his sleeves and was making a good job of the first wall. She was impressed. Clearly he did know his way around a roller and can of paint.

'Didn't anyone ever tell you it was rude to stare?' Gray suddenly enquired, without stopping what he was doing, and Shelby jumped in surprise.

'How did you know I was here?'

Gray cast a glance over his shoulder, eyes locking with hers. 'Your perfume. I'd know the scent of you anywhere. Even over paint fumes.'

Her mouth went dry, and consequently her voice was a tad husky when she spoke. 'I'll have to remember that if ever I want to sneak up on somebody.'

His lips twitched, eyes taking on that roguish gleam. 'You have an open invitation to sneak up on me any time you like, once this is all over,' he informed her in a highly sensual undertone, and her breathing went haywire.

She arched her brows delicately. 'And why would I want to do a crazy thing like that?'

Gray laughed and turned back to his work. 'Because you want me, Red, just about as much as I want you.'

Shelby couldn't help but give a swift backward glance in case anyone had overheard that nerve-tingling remark. Gray hadn't blurted out that they were lovers this time, but from the way her girls watched them both she knew Paula had been on the phone the instant they had left the other house.

She walked a few paces into the room. 'Would you please keep your voice down!' she commanded, wincing inwardly. Things were getting out of hand and she didn't like it.

This time he turned right around to face her. 'Why? They know, and we both know they know.'

'They wouldn't know anything if you'd kept your mouth

shut. Oh, this is impossible, I can't trust you.' Shelby wailed.

Gray's blue eyes turned steely and there was a hard set to his jaw. 'You can trust me to keep you safe from harm, and that's what I'm doing.'

Shelby threw her arms wide. 'What harm? It's been two days and nothing has happened. Nothing is going to happen, either. I hate this, I hate having to be so close to you!'

Something wild flashed into his eyes. 'No, you don't. What you hate is liking having me close to you. Stop lying to yourself, Red,' he returned bluntly. 'As for the other... Two days is nothing. Even two months of nothing would be too short a time for someone with a grudge and time on his hands. Until we catch him, the danger remains real.'

She knew when she was flogging a dead horse again. 'No wonder you and Dad work so well together. You're two of a kind.'

'You mean handsome, charming and witty?'

'No, pigheaded,' she retorted as she turned and walked from the room.

Hidden from view, Shelby cast a frowning look over her shoulder. He was right, she did hate herself for wanting him so much. Having him so near was pure temptation. It made her forget why she had vowed she would never fall for his lies again. Only this time she could see the desire he had for her, and it wasn't fake. Any relationship they had would be based on mutual attraction. She could have that and know that it was real. It wasn't love, but she wasn't so foolish as to expect that from him. Her heart, though, wanted more, and if she did have an affair with Gray, her heart was going to end up even more bruised and battered. Would it be worth it? Quite honestly, right that second, she didn't know.

By late afternoon all that could be done that day had been accomplished, and Shelby stood back to survey the work with a deep sense of satisfaction. Things were really beginning to take shape now. Gray helped to clear things up ready for the next day. Then, after Shelby had spoken to her assistants about what to do next, she called it a day.

She found Gray waiting for her by the front door. He was leaning against the wall with his eyes closed, his face the colour of putty, and her stomach gave an anxious lurch. 'Are you OK?'

Opening his eyes, he straightened up. 'Just a bit of a headache. Nothing to worry about.'

'Have you taken anything?' She knew from experience there was nothing worse than a pounding headache and working with paint fumes could exacerbate it.

'I've got something back at the flat.'

A memory struck her. 'Is it a migraine?' She seemed to recall him suffering them once.

'If I get the medicine in time, it should stop it developing into a migraine.'

Shelby had never suffered from them, but she knew from friends how debilitating it could be. Which was why she didn't waste time talking, but urged him out of the house and into her car. The headache didn't stop him taking all necessary precautions, though, which made her want to scream. Eventually, they were away and she made as good time as she could back to her flat.

Once there, Gray disappeared into the spare bedroom. She left him to it and did her usual daily checks of the phone and emails. She spent an hour in her workroom-cum-office, answering messages and working on plans, and it wasn't until some time later that she realised the flat was silent. Which was unusual, because Gray tended to prowl around from time to time.

Curious, she went in search of him and discovered him lying on the bed, one arm bent across his eyes. She bit her lip at the whiteness around his lips that spoke of the pain he was suffering.

'Is it very bad?' she asked sympathetically, feeling useless.

'I've had worse. The medication will kick in properly soon,' he answered tautly, and she winced.

Recalling that light was a problem for migraine sufferers, she crossed to the window and drew the curtains. 'Better?'

'Some, thanks.'

Shelby approached the bed, hating to see him laid low like this. 'You're very tense. That can't be helping. Let me give you a massage to relieve the tension.'

He looked at her from under his arm and she was sure he was going to refuse, but then he sighed and rolled over on to his stomach. 'Knock yourself out,' he invited.

Kicking off her shoes, Shelby carefully knelt on the bed and placed her hands on his shoulders. They were so tight that to begin with she hardly made any headway, but by persevering she gradually began to notice a difference. Concentrating hard, she worked out kinks along his spine, across his shoulders and up his neck into his hairline. As the tension oozed out of him, Gray began to utter soft sounds of pleasure.

'Hmm, you have magic fingers,' he sighed, catching his breath as she dealt with another knot.

Smiling to herself, Shelby continued her ministrations. After a while he simply lay there, and it wasn't very long after that that she realised the rhythmical sounds coming from him confirmed that he had actually fallen asleep. Arms and fingers aching, she crept off the bed, retrieved her shoes and left him alone. It gave her quite a kick to know she had helped him to feel better, and she went to make herself a cup of tea feeling a righteous sense of satisfaction.

She had just finished drinking it when the phone rang

and, not wanting Gray to be disturbed, she snatched up the receiver before it could ring again. The caller was the owner of an antique shop she used quite regularly.

'Hi, Shelby,' the woman greeted her. 'You know you were looking for vases for your fireplace. Well, I think I've found the very thing you're after. There has been some interest in them, though, so you'd better get over here and have a look.'

Shelby pulled a face as she turned to look at the closed door behind which Gray lay sleeping. He wouldn't want her to go without him, and yet she was loath to wake him now. On the other hand, it would only take her an hour at most to get to the shop and back again. Nothing was going to happen, and she would be back before he woke, so he would never know.

'I'll be right over,' she promised, and hung up the phone.

It was the work of a moment to gather up her jacket, handbag and car keys, then she let herself out of the flat as quietly as a mouse. Feeling like a schoolgirl playing hookey, she laughed softly as she took the lift down to the garage.

She wasn't laughing some hours later, though, as she finally pulled back into her parking spot. She had reached the shop without trouble and, as the owner had promised, the vases were just what she wanted. She had paid for them and left for home, feeling highly pleased with herself. The vases sat proudly on the seat beside her as she drove along, and she had been wondering how she could explain their sudden appearance at her flat without giving herself away when she had hit the traffic. It was snarled up for miles around and, try as she might, she hadn't been able to find a way round whatever the problem was. She had ended up sitting in her car for over an hour, her mobile still on the mantelpiece where she had left it, knowing that there was no way that Gray would stay sleeping so long. She was going to be in trouble. *Big trouble*!

Which proved to be the case. Gray must have discovered her car was gone and had been looking out for her, because he was in the lift when she walked towards it. Her heart sank at the grim look on his face.

'I know you're mad,' she declared swiftly, hoping to head him off. 'But I can explain.'

That narrowed his eyes as he crossed his arms. 'You can explain? OK, try me.'

Shelby's heart skipped a beat, but she waited to speak until after the lift was carrying them both upwards. 'How's your head?' she asked and could have sworn she heard his teeth grind.

'My head is fine. Don't change the subject,' he went on doggedly, and she thought she knew how his squaddies would have felt when they incurred his wrath.

'My guess is there was a really serious accident, because the traffic was stacked up like you'd never believe,' she told him in a rather breathless rush. It got her nowhere.

'And this, somehow, makes it all OK, does it?' he growled, to which she tried a casual shrug.

'I would have been back otherwise,' she explained simply, walking out of the lift ahead of him and pulling a face that he couldn't see.

'So, if you had made it back before I woke, everything would have been OK?' They entered the flat and he shut the door forcefully behind them. 'Of all the downright stupid things you've ever done, this is the worst. I could wring your silly little neck for you! What in hell did you think you were doing?'

'Picking up these vases,' she declared brightly, holding them up for him to see. 'A contact phoned me whilst you were asleep and, as I didn't want to wake you, I simply popped out to collect them. Aren't they just perfect for the fireplace?'

His response to that was to swear, and Shelby jumped so much she nearly dropped her precious vases. Hastily she set them down on the sofa where they would be safe.

'When is it going to get through to you that your life has been threatened, Red? What you did was irresponsible and reckless. Not to mention downright selfish,' Gray railed at her and, because she knew he was right, she got angry too.

'Oh, come on. We both know nothing's going to happen to me.'

His hands opened and closed several times as if he was fighting the urge to shake her till her teeth rattled. 'No. We don't know that. You have no right to play fast and loose with your life and worry the people who care about you. I thought you had more sense than that, but I can see I was wrong.'

The reference to her father stung, as it was meant to do, and she raked an uneasy hand through her hair. 'OK, OK, I agree I shouldn't have done it, but nothing happened, so can we let it go now?'

He looked at her for a long moment, then took a deep wrathful breath. 'Only if I have your solemn word you won't do anything like it again,' Gray returned hardily, and she stared at him in frustration.

'I don't like being kept a prisoner in my own home,' she complained, though she knew it was an exaggeration.

Gray's expression said he knew it too. 'That's coming it too strong. Nobody's stopping you going out, you just don't go alone. You're making this far harder than it need be. So, what's it going to be? Do I have your word?'

'Yes, if it means anything,' she agreed grudgingly.

Having gained her acquiescence, Gray relaxed his angry stance a little. 'It doesn't have much value right now. You have to prove it's worth more,' he told her bluntly as he headed for the kitchen. 'I'm making tea; do you want a cup?'

'Yes, thank you. Milk, no arsenic,' she retorted, regaining some of her spirit, which had been rather quashed in the face of his justifiable anger.

'Don't tempt me,' he shot back immediately and, realising she had got off lightly, Shelby thought it wise to make herself scarce for a while and went off to work in her office.

The mood between them was rather strained for the rest of the evening. They ate together, but conversation was somewhat stilted. She didn't like it, and regretted that she had been the cause of the worsening state of affairs.

It was probably her troubled conscience that made her so restless that night. After an hour or two of tossing and turning with only brief snatches of sleep, she threw back the covers and sat up. It was hopeless. She needed something to help her drop off. Coffee would only keep her awake and she didn't care for milky drinks, but there was always the crossword. It was guaranteed to have her eyes crossing in next to no time.

She had left the newspaper on the coffee table but, so as not to disturb Gray, she decided to pick it up and take it to the kitchen. Having worn her grey cotton vest and shorts to bed tonight, she didn't bother to put on her robe, but padded about as she was.

With the curtains drawn, at Gray's insistence, there was very little light in the lounge. Not surprisingly, Shelby stubbed her toe on the coffee table, stifled a yelp of pain and hopped about on one foot rubbing at the injured digit. That was when, out of the corner of her eye, she saw a dark shadow detach itself from the deeper shadows by the wall and head straight towards her. Caught like a rabbit in the headlights of a car, she stared in horror as the shadow took on a human outline, but she barely had time to open her mouth to scream when it launched itself at her, catching her around the arms and carrying her down on to the nearby sofa. Terrified, and unable to move her arms, she did the only thing she could do and screamed out.

'Gray! Help me! Oh, God...!'

That was all she was able to utter as a large male hand was pressed over her mouth, but it left one arm free and she used it to pound at the back of her attacker. At the same time she thrashed around wildly with her legs, kicking out, and knew she had landed a painful blow when the man on top of her grunted in pain.

Her movements unsettled them and they rolled off the sofa on to the floor, thrusting the coffee table out of the way. Silently she screamed for Gray to come and help her, then set about trying to save herself. There was little she could do. He had stopped her kicking by winding his legs around hers, but his hand had slipped slightly, enough for her to get a good grip with her teeth and bite down hard.

'Ouch!' the man yelped, releasing her mouth, and she took swift advantage.

'Gray! Gray! Help me!' she yelled at the top of her voice, before her breath was taken away when her attacker rolled them over, subduing her with his weight.

'Stop yelling, for the love of Mike, or you'll wake the whole neighbourhood!' a familiar voice growled in her ear.

Shock sent her heart lurching in her chest. 'Gray?' she croaked out in disbelief.

'Right here,' he confirmed, and she could hear the irony in his voice.

Sick fear turned to righteous anger as she slowly realised that her attacker was none other than Gray himself. 'I could kill you. What were you playing at? I was absolutely terrified!'

'That was the general idea,' he retorted mockingly. 'Perhaps now you'll take the situation you're in seriously. That could have been someone else tonight. Someone who wanted to do you serious harm.'

Fury surged up in her like an exploding volcano. 'So you thought that gave you the right to scare me half to death? Get off me, you brute,' she added for good measure, and it was the laugh he gave that tipped her over the edge.

Gray had freed her arms and she was able to rain down blows wherever she could reach, whilst at the same time writhing in an attempt to get him off her. He was far too strong to move, however, and in no time she was exhausted, but she managed to land a good few blows before he could capture her wrists and hold her hands to the floor on either side of her head.

'Don't expect me to apologise, Red,' Gray told her bluntly. 'I just gave you a lesson you needed to learn.'

Shelby glared up at him bitterly, able to see that it was him now that her eyes had adjusted to the light. 'It was a despicable trick,' she snapped, and because his head was just above hers she could see his teeth flash as he grinned.

'So you lost a life. You've got eight others. And you needn't bother complaining to your father. He agreed you needed a salutary lesson.'

'You spoke to him?' she gasped.

'What did you think I would do when I found you missing? I had to check out all the places you might have gone, and your father was first on the list,' Gray explained and her heart sank to her boots.

'So Dad was in on this?' How could he? She felt... betrayed.

'He agreed something had to be done. The method he left up to me. Even I didn't know what I was going to do until I heard you come out of your room tonight. I was already in the lounge, so I took the opportunity to give you a scare,' he enlightened her drolly. 'I'm happy to say you surprised me, Red. You fought like a wildcat.'

She was too angry to be mollified by the praise. 'If I'd known it was you, I would have scratched your eyes out!'

'Cheer up. You've almost certainly given me a black eye,' he returned, pressing the spot on his cheekbone and wincing.

'Does it hurt?' Shelby asked, with false contrition.

'Like hell.'

'Good,' she said with satisfaction. 'Now get off me.'

'Why? I'm quite comfortable,' he countered in a faintly husky voice, and her eyes shot to his.

She could see the faint glitter in his eyes and her stomach lurched. She had been too busy fighting to be aware of him, but now that they lay still his position on top of her made her think of other things entirely. Her anger ebbed away as she slowly became aware of the sensual pleasure of having his body pressed so closely to hers. Her mouth dried up as her body reacted to his. Deep inside a pulse began to beat insistently as her blood surged through her veins and her breasts swelled, her nipples turning into aching buds that longed for more pressure, not less.

The air about them became charged, waiting, expectant, and in the stillness of the room she could hear her ragged breathing mingling with his.

'Maybe…' She started to speak, but then his head lowered and his lips brushed the line of her jaw, and all at once she forgot what she was going to say.

Again and again his lips brushed like butterfly wings up towards her chin, stealing her breath away at the shivery delight. There they paused, hovering over her lips as if debating whether to kiss her or not. Silently her body screamed yes, and she looked at him from beneath weighted lids. Then, just when she thought it wasn't going to happen, Gray uttered a strangled sound and lowered his lips to hers.

It was like magic, the gentle touch out of proportion to

the reaction which went on inside her. She had waited such a long time for this to happen again that for a second or two she actually felt dizzy. It was everything she remembered, and more. His lips explored hers in tantalisingly soft brushes, but then his tongue swept across the same spot, tasting her, and Shelby gasped, her lips parting at this newest pleasure to bombard her system. Immediately he took advantage of the situation to deepen the kiss, his tongue gliding between her lips to begin a sensual exploration.

Shelby gave a sighing moan as she angled her head the better to accommodate him. Shivers of pure delight travelled along her nerve endings, instantly arousing, and she met his tongue with her own, engaging in a dual that stoked the fire until it threatened to burst into flames. She had no intention of stopping, for she wanted to experience this, to know all there was to know about making love to Gray, but he had other ideas. From somewhere he found the strength to break the kiss and pull away enough to look down at her.

'I shouldn't have done that,' he confessed none too steadily. Rolling off her, he sat up.

Shelby sat up beside him, feeling bereft because he was no longer touching her. 'No, you shouldn't,' she agreed gruffly.

He glanced sideways at her. 'Why didn't you push me away?' he asked curiously, and she was glad the darkness hid the flush on her cheeks.

'Put it down to temporary madness,' she riposted dryly.

'This situation is enough to drive anyone insane, Red,' he agreed ironically as he rose to his feet and held out a hand to help her up. 'It's late, we'd better get some sleep.' Sighing, she allowed him to pull her to her feet. 'Have you learned your lesson?'

'Oh, yes,' Shelby agreed, turning away before he could catch a glimpse of her expression.

She *had* learned a lesson tonight, but not the one he thought. She had learned that despite everything that had happened between them, she was still beyond hope where he was concerned. He only had to touch her and she forgot all the reasons why she shouldn't let it happen. He had kissed her, and all thought of fighting him had vanished like morning mist.

She took the memory of that back to bed with her. As she lay there, recalling every vivid second of it, she knew he was her destiny. Her life was inextricably bound with his, and it was time she stopped fighting fate.

CHAPTER SIX

THE next day was pretty much the same as the previous one, only this time Shelby didn't make any solo trips. The vases did look good on the fireplace, and Gray wisely forbore to mention how they had been acquired. A strained peace settled over them.

They were back at her apartment by late afternoon, and Shelby was busy getting her notes up-to-date and writing herself reminders of what she had to do tomorrow, when the telephone rang.

'Shelby Greer,' she identified herself into the receiver and waited for a response. When it didn't come, she held the receiver away from her ear and frowned at it, as if that would make a difference, then tried again. 'Hello, this is Shelby Greer. How can I help you?'

Again there was no answer but, for a second, she thought she could hear breathing before there came the sound of the receiver at the other end being carefully replaced. She blinked in surprise and slowly returned the receiver to its rest.

'What's wrong?' Gray wanted to know. He had been standing by the window staring out, but when she glanced his way she saw he was now watching her.

She shrugged. 'Nothing, really. They just hung up without saying anything, that's all.'

Gray took his hands from his trouser pockets and came over to her, a frown etched on to his brow. 'You actually heard the phone go down?' he asked sharply, and her nerves skittered.

'Yes, I did. And, before that, I could swear I heard

breathing,' she added, and even before she had finished speaking he had taken up the phone and was busily dialling.

When his first call was fruitless he dialled another number and had a briefly worded conversation with someone at the other end. Then he set the phone down and waited. Shelby had no trouble picking up his tension, and the reason for it sprang instantly to mind.

'Do you think it was him?' she asked shakily. This was the first time she had had contact with the person who was making threats against her. It made it real suddenly.

'Unless you're in the habit of receiving hoax calls,' he said by way of confirmation.

Shelby pressed a hand to her stomach, which suddenly felt rather queasy. 'He's never contacted me directly before. Why would he do that?'

Gray looked at her steadily and didn't hold back the truth. 'Because he's upping the stakes. This is what I was afraid of.'

Her breathing grew ragged and her heart was racing like mad. Unable to sit still, she stood and paced about the small room. 'You think I'm in even more danger now?'

He nodded solemnly, not troubling to remind her that he had always thought she was in danger. 'Unless we get a lucky break and the friend I called can trace the call. The hope was to catch him before he put his words into action. Seems as if we're going to have to go to plan B.'

She was rapidly coming to realise that she had taken the whole thing far too casually. 'We're on plan A at the moment, then?' she asked, and received a nod of assent. 'What's plan B, and is there a plan C?'

'Plan B is to get you away from here to a safe place,' he informed her in the serious tone she was used to getting from him.

'Is there such a place?' Suddenly she didn't feel as if she could be safe anywhere.

He must have picked up something in her tone, for he gave her an encouraging smile. 'I know of several, but don't worry, I intend to keep you safe and well. You'll be OK. Trust me.'

'I do,' she replied honestly. The instant she said it, she knew it was true. It was because she trusted him that he had hurt her before.

He stared at her for a moment, a strangely arrested look on his face, then he smiled. 'Good. That should make plan C easier to accomplish.'

'You think it will come to that? We'll have to go to plan C?'

He shrugged. 'You never can tell, but it's best to keep the option open.'

The telephone rang again and Gray snatched up the receiver. He listened intently and Shelby could see from the expression on his face that it was not good news.

'They couldn't trace the call,' he told her when he hung up the phone.

Feeling chilly, Shelby ran her hands along her arms, trying to instil some warmth into them. 'Do you have any idea who this man is?'

'Oscar had been able to narrow it down to a handful of possibles. Of those, one has dropped out of sight. This is the one we're concentrating on,' he enlarged, surprising her, for she hadn't known any of this. Then again, she hadn't taken it seriously. If she had, maybe her father would have told her.

'Does he have a name?'

'Keith Mobley. Does it ring any bells? He has some pretty radical ideas, which your father refused to print in his papers. Mobley didn't take kindly to that and threatened to make him pay.'

Shelby shuddered. 'Why wasn't I told all this?'

'Oscar chose to keep the full details from you because he didn't want to worry you.'

She could almost hear her father telling everyone, Don't tell Shelby. He wanted to protect her, but it had meant she hadn't taken the threat seriously. One creepy phone call had changed that. 'What do we do now?'

'Exactly what we have been doing, only more so. Meanwhile, I'll set the wheels in motion for getting you away. Are you OK with that, or are we going to have a fight about it?' he asked her ironically.

She shook her head. 'My fighting days are over,' she declared vehemently, only to hear him laugh.

'That will be the day.'

Shelby cast him an indignant glare. 'I shall be as good as gold from now on,' she promised, which once again failed to have the desired effect.

His eyes carried that familiar roguish gleam she rather enjoyed seeing. 'Not too good, I hope,' he goaded and she folded her arms with a huff.

'I'm being serious now, Gray!'

His smile appeared. 'Honey, so am I.'

Her hands slapped down on her thighs in a helpless gesture, and she was just about to take issue with him when she realised what he was doing. 'OK, I get it. You're trying to distract me.'

Gray's lips twitched. 'You *were* looking a little frantic.'

Shelby shifted uncomfortably. 'Yes, well, I suddenly realised that anything could have happened to me whilst I wasn't taking the threat seriously. It was a lesson. I'm sorry I gave you and Dad such a hard time.'

Thankfully for her pride, Gray didn't say, I told you so. 'Tell him that next time you see him. Now, if you've finished with the phone for a while, I'd like to make some calls.'

'Could you use the one in the lounge? I still have work to do.'

'Sure, no problem,' he agreed, and left the room.

Shelby sat down at her desk, but it was a while before she could concentrate on her work. She felt foolish for not believing her father. He wouldn't make a fuss about nothing, and she should have accepted that long before this. She owed him a very big apology. Not to mention Gray, who had had to take all the flak.

Eventually she managed to get back to her designs, and was amazed to find hours had passed when she finally shut her computer down. The flat sounded quiet and, curious, she went in search of Gray. She found him sitting at the end of the couch, talking into the telephone. He put it down after a moment or two and must have sensed her presence for he glanced up as she walked towards him. One eyebrow raised questioningly.

'Everything OK?'

Shelby looked at him, really looked, and saw the strain and tiredness around his eyes and mouth. His concern was etched there, and she was annoyed with herself for not seeing it before.

'I'm fine. How are you? You look…tired,' she asked in return, sinking down on to the seat beside him.

He shrugged that off. 'I'll be fine as soon as we catch this creep. He's gone to ground. Talk about *déjà vu*!' he added in an undertone, rubbing a hand around the back of his neck, easing the strain.

Shelby bit her lip. She had forgotten that this was not the first time he had been through something like this. Her attitude must have given him nightmares.

'Was it like this that other time?' she asked, and when his head shot round she hastened to qualify her question. 'I'm not just being nosy. I would like to know what we're up against.'

His jaw set. 'I prefer not to talk about it. Brings back too many bad memories,' he returned grimly, and she leant towards him.

'Have you ever talked to anyone? Shared the pain? Bottling it up can't help,' she probed gently, and his mouth twisted wryly.

'It's hardly a topic for conversation at dinner.'

'True,' Shelby proceeded carefully. 'But there's just the two of us here. Can't you talk to me? I'm a good listener, and I have a vested interest. Besides, I've made things worse for you, and I would very much like to put that right. Please talk to me, Gray,' she pleaded earnestly, and he sighed, closing his eyes, leaning his head against the back of the couch.

'It's not pretty,' he told her in a low voice.

'I can handle that. Believe me, I don't have to have everything sugar-coated,' she returned equally softly. 'Who was being threatened?'

Gray ran his hands over his face, as if to ease the stress of remembering. 'The family of an old friend. We were in one of those warring African states. Piet had something the rebels wanted, but he refused to hand it over.' He took a deep breath. 'So they threatened his wife and children. Piet called for my help, but I failed him.' The statement was made with such bitter self-recrimination that it made her gasp.

'What do you mean, you failed him? I don't believe it,' she protested, instinctively protective, and he looked at her with angry eyes.

'What would you call it when I let his wife die?' Gray demanded grittily, and shock was a lump of ice in her stomach.

'H-his w-wife?' she stammered, and his lips twisted into an ugly line.

'I told you it wasn't pretty,' he grated, and Shelby drew in a steadying breath.

'Tell me,' she urged, knowing it was not as simple as that. Could not possibly be.

Gray leant forward, head bent over his knees. 'Maybe we should leave it there,' he suggested, but she couldn't, for his sake.

'How did she die?'

He glanced at her sideways in silent debate, then sat back again. 'It happened when Piet was away making the arrangements to get his family out. The rebels broke into the compound one night and set fire to the house. We'd had no rain. Everything was a tinderbox. In minutes we had an inferno. I had been sleeping at the front of the house; Jen and the children were at the back. The children were nearest, so I went for them...' Gray's voice tailed off, and Shelby knew what was coming. He took a long breath before continuing. 'I got them out, but when I tried to go back for Jen, I couldn't get in. I don't know how many times I tried before some neighbours managed to pull me away. I failed.'

Shelby's eyes burned with unshed tears, and she drew in a ragged breath as she absorbed his pain. It was the most tragic thing she had ever heard. 'You didn't fail. You saved the children,' she said unevenly, placing a soothing hand on his arm.

'Jen died,' he returned harshly, and she bit her lip, wiping away a tear before it fell.

'Yes, she died, but you saved her precious children. She would have wanted you to do that. Any mother would. You didn't *let* her die. It was a tragedy that could have been so much worse. You've got to forgive yourself, Gray. There's only so much any one man can do, and you did it.' Her heart ached. She wanted to hug him until all his pain was gone, but could only sit there, watching.

Gray didn't respond immediately. Instead, he rose to his feet and crossed to the window, looking out, though Shelby doubted he saw much. Finally, he spoke over his shoulder.

'Now do you see what a determined person can do?' he asked her, and she sighed.

'Yes, and I'm sorry for the crass things I said.' She had just wanted to hurt him as he had hurt her. She hadn't known what she was dealing with.

He turned to her then, expression determined. 'If you mean what you say, then the best apology you can make would be to watch out for yourself.'

Shelby stood up, holding his eyes with her own. 'I will. Thank you for telling me.'

Gray closed the gap between them, reaching out to tuck a stray twist of hair behind her ear. 'You were right, you are a good listener.'

She smiled faintly as her heart expanded with pleasure that she had been able to help him in some small way. 'I'm glad I could help. Listen, I'm going to grab a quick shower before dinner. Shall we order something in?'

He smiled for the first time in ages. 'Leave it to me.'

Shelby retreated to her bedroom. What an awful thing to have happened. Her heart went out to him. The knowledge that he lived with that on his conscience made her want to cry. Nobody deserved to feel such pain. Especially not Gray.

How she wished she could have gone to him and held him, but that was impossible. All she could do was listen and try to heal the wound. She knew all about wounds, having one of her own. Because of it she had carried a grudge, and what good had it done her? So what if Gray didn't love her? To say no to what he was offering would be cutting off her nose to spite her face.

She was, above all else, a realist. You couldn't love to order, nor make someone love you. And though that often made her heart ache, given a choice, she would rather have this moment with him now than a lifetime of nothing. *Carpe diem*. It was that simple. Seize the day. Life was short, and who knew what was around the corner. So she would take what she could. There would be time enough later for regrets. At least this way she would always have some good memories to warm her heart in the long winter of the rest of her life.

The following morning Gray didn't reveal much about the plans he had been making the night before. All he would tell her over the breakfast table was that they were progressing nicely and, with luck, they would be leaving within the next few days. They could have gone now, but he wanted the security checked out first.

Shelby tried to play twenty questions, to get some idea of where they would be going, but all she got in response was a smile and a shake of the head. Finally she sighed testily. 'How will I know what clothes to take if you don't tell me where we're going?' she complained with feminine logic, and received a long look for her pains.

'It's summer, Red. Take a wild stab at what clothes you'll need,' he suggested dryly, and she very nearly threw her cup at him. 'What plans do you have for today?'

'I need to spend time on the Tyrwhit-Jones woman's design. Lord, I keep thinking of her as the Awful Antonia. It would be just my luck to say it to her face. What else? Oh, yes, I have to call in on another client in the wilds of deepest Sussex. She isn't quite sure about something, so I promised to put it right. We'd better do that first. I'll drive.'

Two hours later they finally left suburbia behind and could bowl along the fairly empty country roads. The only car in sight was the one far behind them.

'Connie's a dear, but she lives in the back of beyond!' Shelby exclaimed, though not really complaining.

'Connie?'

'Lady Constance Cosgrove. Connie to her friends. You'll adore her. She's the friendliest natured woman you'll ever meet.' Pausing, she cast him a twinkling look. 'She'll adore you, too. She's the most dreadful flirt. No handsome man is safe.'

Shelby glanced into the rear-view mirror and frowned. The car which had been some way behind them appeared to be closing the gap rapidly. Thinking the driver wanted to pass, she slowed down to give him room, but he tucked in behind her with scarcely room to breathe. So she sped up, whereupon the other car did the same, keeping itself dangerously close.

'What's he doing?' she asked sharply, and Gray glanced round. What he saw made him swear and turn back to her.

'We need to get off the road. Look around for a drive… anything. Hurry!' he urged her, glancing back again.

Shelby's heart leapt into her throat. A quick glance in the mirror showed the car looming large behind them. She didn't have to ask who or what, she knew. It was him! Somehow he had followed them from the city and whatever he had in mind didn't bode well. Trying not to panic, she searched for somewhere they might go to get away from their pursuer, but before she could do so there was an almighty crash from behind which jerked her backwards and forwards. The car swerved dangerously across the road and it was only with Gray's help that they straightened up.

Minutes later the man drove his car into their rear for a second time and again they fought to stay on the road. Shelby searched frantically for somewhere to pull off, but up ahead the road opened up with fields on either side.

'What shall I do?' she cried to Gray, who was watching the car swerve out and speed up alongside them.

'Brace yourself!' he shouted above the noise, just as the

other car swerved violently, crashing into the side of them, sending them plunging off the road.

The car bucked and leapt over deep ruts that jarred her spine. Up ahead, someone had been digging out a fallen tree, leaving an enormous hole in the ground, and they were heading straight for it. Braking like fury, she struggled with the wheel, but there had been rain recently and the earth had turned to mud. Unable to gain purchase, the car shot sideways into the hole with enough force for her head to slam into the window.

A black hole opened up before her and she tumbled into it, knowing no more.

Shelby stirred, eventually, a few days after the accident which had brought her to the hospital bed she lay in. Not that she knew it was a few days—or what kind of bed she was in to begin with. She wasn't really aware of anything much, except that the world seemed a little fuzzy around the edges, and she hadn't even opened her eyes yet.

She accomplished this with surprising difficulty. It seemed her eyelids were carrying lead weights, and she couldn't imagine why. That was her first inkling that something wasn't quite right. The second followed fast on the heels of the first. Her nose was assailed by an unmistakable scent that meant only one thing—hospital.

She was in hospital? What on earth was she doing there? The as yet only mildly alarming and rather more intriguing realisation had her automatically trying to check out her limbs for movement. The discovery that, firstly, she could barely move and, secondly, that even a small amount sent a shaft of pain through her head, caused her to desist immediately.

Well, at least she knew what she was doing here, she mused wryly, taking short breaths to ease the pain, which thankfully began to fade away. She must have had a run in with something a great deal larger than herself —and come off the worst for it. However, her attempt to recall the event did nothing but make the headache increase. It seemed to have turned her thought processes to mush at the same time. Anyway, it took too much effort to think right now. She would reminisce later.

What she could do was take a much more careful inventory of her injuries. Bracing herself for pain, she managed to raise her arms and legs some inches off the mattress, which reassured her that her body was intact, even if it was one big aching bruise.

'It's OK, you're all in one piece,' a familiar male voice declared from somewhere on her right, giving her an almighty shock, for she had believed herself to be alone. 'Sadly, I can't say the same for your car,' the voice added dryly.

'Gray?' she queried faintly, turning her head in the direction she thought his voice emanated from, but he was just beyond her field of view. 'What on earth are *you* doing here?'

'Keeping an eye on you, of course,' he came back with his usual irony, which she didn't have the strength to make a riposte to right then.

'Oh! When did you get back?' By rights he should have been on the other side of the world.

'Back?' Gray countered somewhat cautiously, and she sighed.

'You were in Sydney the last I heard,' she reminded him a little testily, because her body hurt every time she moved. The next instant she heard a creaking of furniture as her companion stood up.

'The Sydney business was cleared up quickly,' he informed her evenly.

Shelby loved the rich texture of his voice. Loved him, full stop. His looks matched his voice, and so far as she was concerned he was the sexiest thing on two legs. It was a pity he had proved to be such a louse. As ever, though, being close to him sent a tingle through her system. Or maybe that was just the painkillers wearing off.

His presence partially explained, she struggled to recall something odd he had just said. 'My car?'

'The one you crashed in your attempt to avoid hitting a dog,' Gray invented cautiously, checking out a theory.

Shelby frowned. She didn't remember crashing the car. The dog didn't register either. 'Did I hurt anyone?' she croaked, and tried to swallow, but her mouth was as dry as a desert.

'Only yourself,' he informed her, stepping into sight. Her lack of contradiction was setting off alarm bells like crazy.

Unaware of his concerns, Shelby had her own path to follow. Oh, yes, she thought for the umpteenth time, he was sexy all right. Black-haired and handsome as the devil. All she could actually see was his top half, but that was more than enough to impress her. He had the kind of chest that invited a woman to snuggle up close. Quite a hunk, in fact. Many a night she had fallen asleep imagining how it would feel snuggling up with him. The one time she had thought dreams would become reality, she had been rudely disillusioned. She had vowed never to forgive him for what he had done.

'Thirsty?' Gray asked, cutting through her bitter meanderings, and she nodded, wincing at the thump the action created.

Gray winced in sympathy. 'You had a lump the size of a goose egg on your head, but it's going down,' he told her as he reached for a button somewhere beyond her vision, but which raised the head of the bed and put her in a more comfortable sitting position. 'Try some of this.'

He was holding out a glass of water, and she allowed him to put it to her lips so that she could drink. It was warm but wonderfully refreshing. When she had had enough she pulled away, risking a faint smile of gratitude.

'Thanks,' she said, her voice sounding much more normal now. 'Seriously, Gray, why are you here? I can imagine Dad hovering by my bedside, but not you.' Unless her father had ordered him to be here. Now that sounded more like it, she thought waspishly.

Gray momentarily froze in the act of replacing the glass on the bedside table. He was worried but dared not show it. If Shelby didn't know why he was here, then she must have a memory problem. That being the case, he couldn't blurt out that she was in danger. He had to be cautious and still try to work out what she did or didn't know. The simplest way to do that was to talk about a supposed change in their relationship and take it from there.

'Why not?' he challenged casually, his eyes watching every flicker of emotion on her face. 'I've always cared what happened to you.'

She frowned in total surprise. 'Since when?' she queried sceptically. She knew exactly how much he didn't care about her. Sluggish as her brain was, it was working enough for her to wonder what he was up to now.

Gray replaced the glass and slipped his hands into the pockets of his jeans. 'For a long time, as it happens, but more recently since we put aside our differences and developed a closer relationship,' he explained, choosing his words with care.

Shelby's lips parted in a tiny gasp of surprise. 'We have?' She wondered if she was still dreaming for, much as she had always wanted more from him, she had learned the hard way that it was like reaching for the moon. To her further surprise, he nodded.

'It's why I'm here, waiting for you to wake up. I didn't expect that when you did you wouldn't remember about us.'

She could feel her eyes grow as round as saucers. 'Us?' The word was little more than a shocked whisper. What was he saying? There had never been an 'us' for them. How could things have changed so suddenly, and how could she not remember it?

Gray carefully picked up one of her hands and held it in his. 'I know it's a lot to take in, Red, but you and I are most definitely us.'

'But we can't be. I'd remember!' she pointed out, staggered by the simple act of his taking her hand. Her mind was reeling. He just didn't do that sort of thing. She had to be going crazy.

His lips twitched, but his expression remained rueful. 'You'd think so, but clearly you don't. I think it must be due to the accident. You had a heck of a bang on the head.'

Because it was the one thing she had always desperately wanted—loving him as she did—she knew it couldn't be true. It had to be a lie. So she shook her head emphatically. 'Oh, no, I don't think so. This is just another rotten game you've decided to play on me. Well, I don't think much of your timing. You and I an item? I'd sooner believe the earth was flat!'

'I'd prove it to you in a way that would expel all your doubts, but you're in no fit state to be kissed,' he assured her, but Shelby shook her head.

His certainty was countered by her own knowledge that he had played such a trick before. 'Kissing me would prove nothing. Why should I believe you, when I know what lengths you can go to?'

Gray sighed, his expression sombre. 'I explained about that. True, your father came to me for help, but I said no. You see, I'd been waiting a long time for you. And when the opportunity arose to change the nature of our relationship, I took it. Unfortunately, Oscar returned and got the wrong end of the stick. You believed him.'

Shelby listened to him in consternation. Oh, she remembered everything so clearly. Gray romancing her, her father telling her it had been at his request. Hurt, she had raged at Gray, because she had believed her father. Now Gray was telling her it had all been a mistake. He hadn't agreed to help her father at all. She hadn't given him a chance to explain. If that were true, then all the time she had spent hating him had been for nothing.

Her heart lurched. Could she have been wrong? 'I believed all this?' she asked doubtfully.

'After we'd discussed it for a while, yes,' he confirmed, watching her carefully.

One thing he said stuck in her mind. 'You've been waiting for me?' It was an incredible thing to believe, but if it were true...

'Just about as long as for ever,' he quipped, smiling faintly.

A lump lodged in her throat and she had to swallow hard to shift it. 'You're serious? This isn't just some, *Let's make a fool out of Shelby* ploy?'

'I am, and it's not.'

'You and I are...?' Understandably, she wasn't quite sure what term to use. Gray supplied one.

'Involved.'

Shelby took a steadying breath, eyes searching his for any hint of a lie. She knew what her heart wanted to believe. Dared she, though? Just on his word? Lord, how she wished she could remember him telling her all this before! She loved him, she should trust him, but she had been wrong before. Except, he was telling her she hadn't been wrong. What did she do?

'This is too incredible!' she exclaimed. She didn't know what to believe. How could she accept what he said at face value? And yet...what if it was completely true?

The sensible thing was to keep an open mind. For now

the only thing she could do was accept what he told her, be cautious and wait for her memory to return. The truth would come out then. So, she could take it on trust for now and let matters take their own course. And if it turned out he was lying…Well, she would deal with that then.

'OK, I accept that what you're telling me may be true. I'll know one way or the other when my memory returns, so you'd better not be lying,' she told him cautiously. She had to protect herself, for her heart was so very vulnerable to him. Please God, let it not be a terrible mistake! 'Is there anything else I should know?' she asked calmly, though the question set her heart thumping anxiously.

'About us? Well, we're still in the exploring stage, Red. Getting to know each other better,' he said, flashing his roguish grin.

Shelby almost howled. After wanting something for so long, it was just her luck that when it finally happened she couldn't remember it! How could fate do this to her? Something must have shown on her face, for Gray reached out and brushed his knuckles gently over her cheek.

'Don't worry about it. Besides, there's another side to look at. We can always start all over again,' he teased gently, then sobered. 'First things first. There are a few things I need to ask you. First and foremost, I take it you do remember your name?'

She managed a faint smile. 'If I can't remember that either, I'm really in trouble. My name is Shelby Greer. How was that? Do I pass?' Her spirit, which had been knocked for six by his revelation, was rallying.

He returned her smile with a slightly ragged one. 'Thankfully, yes. I admit to being worried. OK, we've established you know your name. What is the last thing you remember?'

The last thing? She frowned, probing the mists. 'I remember Dad telling me you'd gone to Australia. That was the last time I saw him.'

Gray nodded, his suspicions well and truly confirmed. 'That was over two months ago, Red. It seems to me that bump on the head has taken away the memory of several weeks of your life.'

It was a shock, even though she had been half prepared for it. 'That long?'

Gray squeezed her hand bracingly. 'Look at it this way, it could have been worse. You could have lost your memory completely.' He lay her hand back on the covers gently. 'Listen, sweetheart, I'm going to leave you alone for a time whilst I go and get a doctor to look at you. I must ring Oscar, too. In the meantime, try not to get too alarmed. I'm sure it must be scary, but try to stay calm. I won't be long.'

He went out, leaving her alone with her thoughts. They were, to put it mildly, in a state of confusion. OK, so she knew people often forgot things after an accident, but it had never happened to her before. It was alarming not being able to recall what had happened just a few days ago. She had no memory of the crash and, what was more important, she had no memory of them! It was so unfair!

Which brought her back to them. Was she accepting the truth of it too quickly? Quite possibly, because she wanted it to be true. Because, for all his faults, she was sure Gray wouldn't lie about this. And yet... She cut the thoughts off, knowing she was going round in circles. It was an impossible situation and the best thing she could do was what he said—remain calm.

Gray, meanwhile, had asked one of the nurses to get hold of Shelby's doctor, and was in the process of phoning her father. As soon as Oscar picked up the phone, he told him the news.

'Shelby's awake.'

'Oh, thank God. Thank God!' Oscar Greer exclaimed emotionally. 'Is she all right?'

'Physically, she has some painful bruising. The trouble is, she appears to have lost her memory of the last few weeks. She doesn't know anything that's been going on. What do you want me to do?'

Her father's response was immediate. 'You can't tell her, Gray. You know Shelby. She'll fight it like she did before, and we don't have time to win her round a second time. You've got to find a way to keep her safe without alarming her. Can you do that?'

Gray grimaced, knowing he had already provided himself with the perfect means of doing so. 'To test her memory, I told her the two of us were an item. She believes it to be true,' he explained, wondering how that would go down with his boss. How Shelby would deal with it in the long term, he didn't dare to contemplate. Time enough for dealing with that when he had to. He just wanted to keep her safe.

Oscar didn't even query it. 'Excellent. You must keep her believing it, my boy. Do whatever you have to do to keep her out of harm's way. Keep her safe for me, Gray.'

'You have my word on that, Oscar. I'll take her away to the country like we planned. You'd better pack some clothes for the pair of us and bring them down with you.'

'Will do. Tell her I love her and that I'll be there as soon as I can. How are you bearing up?'

'Better now she's awake,' Gray admitted. 'I'd better go. I told her I wouldn't be long.'

'I'll let you go. Take care of yourself, Gray. Goodnight.'

Gray said goodnight and hung up the phone. The die was cast. Not the way he had planned it, but he had long ago learned to take a situation as he found it and turn it to his advantage. There were risks involved, but again he was prepared to take them. Not with Shelby's life, though. Priority number one was keeping her out of harm's way. What happened after that—well, he was good at thinking on his feet. All might work out right yet.

CHAPTER SEVEN

SHELBY was just beginning to think she had been abandoned when a doctor, complete with white coat and stethoscope, strode into the room. He sat himself down on the edge of the bed and smiled at her in a friendly way as he examined her with his eyes.

'Awake at last, I see. How do you feel?' he asked in that brisk way doctors had.

'My body aches and my head hurts,' she told him, though her gaze was on Gray, who now entered the room and took up a position by the window. Folding his arms across his chest, he smiled at her encouragingly and gave her a thumbs up.

'Well, that's what you get for driving into a hole in the ground. Fortunately, no irreparable harm was done. We did fear concussion when we saw the size of the lump on your head, but that's reducing nicely. You're a very lucky woman,' the doctor pronounced whilst listening to her heart and taking her pulse. Finally he set her hand down and looked at her soberly. 'I'm told you have a problem remembering.'

He made it sound so everyday that she laughed. 'You could say that. I seem to know everything that has happened up to a few weeks ago. Is that normal?'

'Temporary memory loss after the kind of knock on the head you had is not unusual. In most cases the memory returns after a short while,' the kindly doctor informed her paternally.

'How long must I wait? Days? Weeks?' she wanted to know, and he smiled.

'There is no magic number. When it's ready, your memory will most probably return, though there are some instances where it doesn't, but let's not go there just yet. What I do know is that trying to force it doesn't help. You must learn to be a patient patient,' he added, laughing at his own joke as he rose off the bed. 'I'll arrange for someone to come along and talk to you about it. The dos and donts, as it were. In the meantime, I'll leave you in the safe hands of your..er…um…husband.'

The doctor left, but she didn't notice. His parting words had make her eyes widen. She stared at Gray, still standing by the window, whose expression was wryly amused.

'Husband?' she queried dryly, and he smiled. The action brought warmth and a light of twinkling mischief to his eyes. It also had its usual effect on her. Her heart turned over and a bubble of emotion swelled up inside her. She loved him so much. Beyond reason. Beyond anything. For the moment, at least, he appeared to be hers. That was what he was telling her—but her husband?

'We're not married, but we are living together. I imagine the doctor didn't know what to call me,' Gray teased lightly, inviting her to share the joke, but she was too busy taking in what he had just told her.

'We're living together?' Somehow, in her thinking, she hadn't got them quite that far. They were lovers, then. How cruel not to know it when she'd waited so long.

'At your flat for the present,' Gray confirmed, collecting a chair as he came closer. Setting it by the bed, he pulled out his wallet and searched inside it for a moment before handing over a photograph. 'I thought this might interest you. It was taken at a charity function we both attended,' he enlarged as he sat down and waited for her reaction.

Shelby stared at the photograph. It had obviously been taken at a party, and showed the pair of them standing together, laughing at the camera with raised hands holding glasses of champagne. Her doubts eased a fraction at this tangible proof.

'We seem to have been having fun,' she remarked, handing the photo back. Her throat felt tight. It hurt so much to know that they had finally become lovers and yet she couldn't recall even the simplest kiss or caress.

Gray took the snap and replaced it in his wallet. 'Making up for lost time.'

'We don't fight any more?' she asked curiously.

A wolfish grin tweaked at her heart. 'Not in the same way, no,' he confirmed and Shelby felt her cheeks grow warm.

'You're not going to tell me we're engaged too?' Nothing would surprise her.

'We haven't got around to it yet,' Gray responded, then unfastened the pocket of his shirt and reached into it. 'You do have rings, though.' Holding his hand out palm upwards, he revealed a simple gold wedding band and a solitaire engagement ring. 'Do you recognise them?'

Shelby looked down at the rings and smiled. Abruptly her eyes filled with emotional tears, which she knew must be due mostly to the accident, for she had no memory of their owner, save in a few tattered photographs. 'They were my mother's. Dad gave them to me on my eighteenth birthday.'

'The nurse took them off to clean you up. I've been looking after them until you woke up.' She took the rings he tumbled into her palm and slipped them on to her right hand.

She glanced up, smiling. 'Thank you.'

'You once told me you felt lost without them,' he told her simply, and she sighed, twisting the rings around her finger.

'I do.' She recalled the occasion. He had been holding her hand across a dinner table and the sky hadn't yet fallen in on her dreams. 'It's the only real contact I have with her. I wish I could have known her,' she said softly.

'I should imagine she was very much like you,' Gray declared with a faint smile, and she lifted an eyebrow.

'You mean annoying, self-opinionated and spoilt?' she challenged, using some of the words with which he had described her over the years.

He tutted. 'I was thinking of strong, passionate and compassionate,' he countered pointedly, and her nerves jolted.

'Is that how you really see me?' she asked in surprise. She couldn't recall him ever saying anything so complimentary. Unless you counted the time she'd believed he'd been lying, but which now turned out to have been the truth. A convoluted thought that made her wince inwardly.

'When you're not being the proverbial pain in the backside,' he added, tongue-in-cheek, and Shelby laughed. This was more like she remembered.

'I knew you couldn't change your spots entirely.' Gray laughed too and they shared a moment of total empathy, which left her feeling both uplifted and sad. 'I can't remember this 'us' you talk of.' She tried again, hoping something would miraculously click into place, but nothing happened. It was all still depressingly blank. And her head was beginning to ache with the effort. 'Damn. You'd think something so momentous would do the trick!'

'You can't rush it, Shelby, but I'm not surprised you're trying to. You always were impatient.'

'Well, of course I only have your word for that,' she said dryly, trying to make light of the situation she found herself in, and it brought a wry smile to his lips.

'See, you're sounding more like your old self already! Using every trick in the book to your advantage.'

'Don't start with me, Gray. I'm poorly, remember?' she said faintly, pressing a limp hand to her brow, and that made him laugh again.

'That will only get you so far with me, Red. *I* haven't forgotten anything!' he told her sardonically, and she frowned at him from under her hand.

'How kind of you to remind me. I must try to return the courtesy one day,' she promised direly, but he didn't look in the least worried.

'I'm sure you will, darling,' he agreed with good humour.

The endearment tugged at her heart. It was possible he had said it countless times in the past few weeks, but this was the first time of hearing it for her. 'I like the way you say that,' she told him whimsically, feeling almost shy. It was hard to respond naturally when she wasn't totally sure it wasn't a mistake.

Blue eyes smiled kindly at her. 'What—darling? You'll be hearing it a lot.'

She looked at him a little uncertainly. 'Good. Maybe it will help me believe…' She broke off, biting her lip as she realised her remark was casting doubt on him. Gray merely nodded consideringly.

'Make you believe I'm telling the truth? I hope so.'

About to respond, Shelby found herself unable to hold back a yawn. It had been a fraught few hours, and now she was being overwhelmed by a feeling of exhaustion. 'Lord, I'm tired,' she muttered, closing her eyes. She didn't want to sleep yet. There were so many questions she still had to ask. Her body, however, had other ideas.

Gray pulled his chair up beside the bed, making himself as comfortable as he could. 'Go to sleep, Red. I'll still be here when you wake up,' he promised, and received a breathy little sigh in response.

A few minutes later he could tell from the rhythmical sound of her breathing that she was asleep. He brushed the hair away from her face and raised himself enough to press a soft kiss on her lips.

'Hell, Red,' he declared softly. 'What have we got ourselves into this time? I'm taking a hell of a risk here. All I hope is that, when the dust settles, it will turn out to have been a risk worth taking.'

Sighing, he made himself as comfortable as he could in the chair, placed his hand over hers on the cover, and closed his eyes.

He had to be really uncomfortable, Shelby thought as she stared down at the sleeping figure of Gray in the chair beside her bed. It was dark outside and from the lack of sounds beyond her door she knew it must be late. She must have slept for hours and certainly felt better for it. She had finally awakened to find Gray slumped in the chair, and had lain looking at him ever since.

For the nth time she wished she could remember what had finally brought them together. Her brain had been working overtime since she'd stirred. Sure, Gray had said that he had been attracted to her for a long time, but why had he made no attempt to tell her the truth before if she meant that much to him? The answer made her lips twist. Probably because she had been so busy hating him that she had never given him the chance! Until when? Something must have happened to change that. Something in the last few months. But what? It was so frustrating! What if…? No! She had to stop with the 'what if's. They would drive her mad. She had to wait and see. Had to give herself time.

Looking at him now brought a smile to her lips and gave her a warm feeling around her heart. Gray had hinted that they were lovers, but had she told him she loved him? Did he love her, or was this just an affair? Lord, she hated the not knowing. If only she could remember, she'd have answers to all her questions!

'Trying to make yourself remember generally has the reverse result.' Gray's sleepy voice interrupted her thoughts and she turned her head to look at him. He looked rumpled and dog-tired and endlessly endearing.

'I know, but in my position you'd do the same thing,' she pointed out, and he gave her a lopsided smile of acknowledgement.

'Probably. How are you feeling now?' he asked as he stood up and stretched, trying to smooth out the kinks the chair had put in his body.

'Much better. My head has stopped aching. What time is it?'

He glanced at his watch. 'Way past the witching hour. Getting on for three in the morning. We're probably the only ones awake.' He flexed his back and shoulders, easing the cramped muscles.

'You can't be comfortable in that chair. Why don't you go home?' she suggested, though she didn't relish the thought of being here alone. Hospitals gave her the heebie-jeebies.

'I probably would, if we were anywhere near home,' he agreed with her, and Shelby couldn't contain her surprise.

'Where are we?' She had assumed, obviously wrongly, that she was in her local hospital.

Gray smiled wryly. Now they were coming to the crunch point. He planned to keep as close to the truth as possible, without causing her to smell a rat. Hopefully she would accept the story without question.

'Sussex. We were on our way to visit one of your clients. After that we were going to head off for a holiday.'

'Oh,' she responded faintly, naturally not remembering, though she knew she had a client in the county. 'Have I spoiled our holiday?'

He shook his head. 'Put it off for a few days, that's all. As soon as you can leave hospital, we'll go on our way. You'll need a little rest and TLC after this.'

'How, if I wrecked the car?' she wanted to know, and Gray grinned.

'There are other forms of transport. I called in a favour from a friend,' he informed her, then found himself having to smother a powerful yawn of his own. 'Sorry about that,' he apologised.

'You really need to get some decent sleep, Gray. Why don't you ask if there's a room here you could use?' Shelby said in some concern.

'It's OK. I have a room booked at a nearby hotel. I haven't used it much because I wanted to be here when you woke up,' he explained. Running a hand over his chin, he winced. 'I could do with a shave, too.'

'Well, I'm awake now and you can see I'm fine, relatively speaking. Go. Have a shave, get some sleep and come back later. All I'm going to do is sleep, anyway,' she urged him.

After a moment, when it looked to her as if he might argue, Gray shrugged. 'You're right. I'm out on my feet.' Coming to the bed again, he bent over her. 'See you in the morning, darling,' he said softly and pressed a kiss to her forehead.

When he made to move away, however, he discovered Shelby had grabbed two handfuls of his shirt and was holding on tightly. He looked down into her eyes.

'If you think you're leaving after that, think again. I didn't hurt my lips, you know.'

His eyes dropped to her mouth, and his own lips twitched. 'No, I can see that.' Letting out a sighing breath, he took her lips in a gentle yet provocative kiss that sought a response from her then stopped once he had got it. Drawing back, he smiled wryly. 'Better?'

'Much,' she agreed huskily. The tingling his lips had started still washed along her veins. 'Goodnight,' she said, suddenly reluctant to see him go.

He sensed it and gave her hand a reassuring squeeze. 'Close your eyes and I'll be back before you know it,' Gray promised, and crossed the room in a couple of strides. At the door he paused briefly to give her a wave, then vanished from sight.

Shelby turned her head on the pillow and stared out of the window where the sky was already beginning to lighten in the distance, a faint smile curving her lips. Lifting a hand, she ran a finger over lips that still tingled. Gray must have kissed her in the last few weeks, but this was the only one she remembered. This kiss, brief though it had been, told her a lot. They were an 'us' all right. Another layer of doubts vanished, easing her mind.

Maybe dreams really did come true. On that thought she closed her eyes again and before very long had drifted back to sleep.

Outside in the corridor, where he stood leaning against the wall, Gray rubbed his hands over his face in a battle-weary gesture. He couldn't actually leave until his relief turned up—a good friend he could trust to look out for Shelby whilst he got some much needed rest. Jack was at the hotel and had promised to be there in ten minutes. In the meantime, he waited.

He found himself caught in the sticky web of truths and half-truths he had woven in order to keep Shelby safe. It wasn't going to be easy treading the fine line that had been drawn. She might think they were a couple; yet, however much he wanted her, the one thing he couldn't do was act as if the fiction was a reality. Only a scoundrel would take advantage of the situation and, though appearances were to the contrary, he wasn't a scoundrel.

He laughed wryly. He was going to be in for a hell of a time and he only hoped his self-control would last out. Once he would have been certain, but things had changed and now he wasn't quite so sure.

Shelby was discharged from the hospital forty-eight hours later. There wasn't anything wrong with her that wouldn't heal in time—even her memory. She had spoken to a counsellor and the sensible advice she had been given had helped her a lot.

Gray arrived to pick her up mid-morning. Shelby had been up, champing at the bit, for hours, and she virtually pounced on him when he walked in the door.

'It's about time. I thought you were never going to get here,' she grumbled, and he shot her a resigned look.

'You must be feeling better. You sound more like you already,' he gibed as she grabbed the bag of clothes he had brought with him and started to ransack the contents.

'I'm sorry. I just want to get out of here. I can't stand this place.'

'You never did like hospitals,' a dear voice declared gruffly, and Shelby glanced up in surprise as a tall, greying man stepped into the room.

Tears of emotion sprang to her eyes. 'Dad!' she exclaimed in a choked voice and abandoned the clothes to hurry over to him. 'It's good to see you.'

Oscar Greer smiled and held out his arms. 'It's good to see you awake and alert. The last time I was here you were unconscious. Come and give me a hug. I need it badly. You scared the life out of me.'

'I'm sorry,' Shelby apologised, hugging him tightly.

Oscar released her to arm's length and gave her the once over. 'You're looking much better. Gray has been keeping me appraised of your recovery, but I had to come and see for myself before you went away. Have you remembered anything yet?'

Shelby shook her head. 'Not a sausage. I rang the studio to see how my projects were going and I don't remember doing half of what Paula was talking about. Really I should go and see her before going anywhere,' she declared, going back to her bag of clothes.

Oscar and Gray exchanged a speaking look, and it was Gray who answered.

'Only you're not going to. You're going to obey doctors' orders and take it easy for a while. Understood?'

She had had no intention of doing any such thing, until he tried to take charge. 'You can't order me about, Gray Compton,' she told him, chin raised to a belligerent angle.

He swatted the words away like flies. 'No, but I can throw you over my shoulder and put you in the car. It's your choice. What's it to be?'

Shelby folded her arms and stared at him hard. 'You'd do it too, wouldn't you?'

Blue eyes gleamed back at her. 'In a heartbeat,' he confirmed hardily.

She looked at her father. 'Are you going to let him get away with this?'

Oscar hid a smile behind his hand, then cleared his throat. 'I'm afraid I agree with Gray on this. The girls are fully capable of managing without you for a while.'

'Traitor,' she accused her parent, but knew he was right. She had chosen her assistants because they could work unsupervised. That wasn't the point of the disagreement.

'Now that that's settled,' Gray declared triumphantly, 'I'm going to take Oscar down to the cafeteria for coffee whilst you get changed, OK?'

Shelby shrugged indifferently. 'OK, that's fine. I'll be here. Nowhere else to go!' she retorted grumpily, and scowled when they abandoned her to her mood and walked out again.

Alone, her glum expression soon changed to a catlike smile. He might think he had won, but only because she hadn't been serious about staying. How could he think for one second that she would prefer to stay and work when the opportunity to be alone with him was the alternative? During the last couple of days she had come to terms with the situation. Gray was so attentive, so supportive…so caring, she couldn't believe it was simply a game. So she was heeding her own advice, taking everything as it came and not looking too far ahead.

She could feel excitement building up inside her. It was all due to the fact that she and Gray were going away together. They were going to be alone and, no matter what had happened before, it would be the first time for her. She had dreamed of such a moment. Had longed for it with all her heart, and now it was going to happen. The circumstances could have been better, but she wasn't about to look a gift horse in the mouth.

When Gray and her father returned, Shelby was dressed in jeans, an emerald T-shirt and deck shoes. She had everything packed and waiting on the bed and was pacing the room impatiently. They left immediately, Shelby holding her father's arm, with Gray bringing up the rear with her belongings. She had planned to say goodbye to some of the nurses on her way down but, to her surprise, found herself swept out of the hospital and into a waiting car in a matter of minutes.

'Just a second. I wanted to say thank you to the staff,' she protested as Gray got in beside her, blocking her attempt to clamber back out.

'There isn't time, darling. You have a plane to catch,' Oscar argued reasonably as he took his place beside the driver. 'OK, John. Take it away.'

She subsided because she was not about to fling herself out of a moving vehicle. She would make sure she sent a card and gift for all the staff on her floor to share.

Gray cast a look out of the rear window before making himself comfortable beside her.

'Did we forget something?' Shelby asked curiously, looking back herself, but he shook his head.

'Just checking,' he explained easily. 'Force of habit,' he added, and she sat back again.

'Where are we going?' she queried once they had been driving a while. She knew the area from visits to her client, but couldn't work out where their route would take them.

'The local airport. There's a plane on standby there,' Gray returned smoothly.

She frowned at him, wondering if he had just misunderstood or was being deliberately obtuse. 'I meant, where are going? What's our final destination?'

'It's a surprise,' he divulged noncommittally, and something suddenly struck her as odd, though she couldn't say why.

'Why do I get the feeling something's going on?' she asked, and was surprised when both Gray and her father turned to look at her sharply. Then she found the driver's eyes watching her in the rear-view mirror, which was the most startling thing of all. What on earth…?

It was her father who answered. 'Listen, darling, all that's going on is that Gray arranged this surprise for you. Now, if he tells you, it won't be a surprise. So why don't you stop worrying about nothing and enjoy the journey?' he advised her.

'That's all very well, but I'm not sure that I like surprises,' she argued, momentarily diverted, and everyone laughed, including the driver.

'That one will never fly, sweetheart. We all know there's nothing you love more than springing a surprise on your nearest and dearest,' Gray pointed out mockingly. 'This time, the surprise is on you.'

There was nothing she could say to that. It was, after all, true. Sighing heavily, she made an attempt to concentrate on the passing scenery, and it was as she was doing so that she felt Gray take her hand and thread her fingers through his. She looked round at him questioningly.

'The thought of flying makes me nervous,' he told her, and her eyebrows rose incredulously.

'I happen to know that you have your own pilot's licence,' she countered dryly.

He grinned faintly. 'OK, the truth is I needed an excuse to hold your hand.'

'You've never needed an excuse to do anything in your entire life,' she pointed out, but didn't take her hand away. It felt good. Right. She probably held his hand all the time these days, and one day it would all come back to her.

Gray looked at her, a strange light in his eyes. 'Haven't I? You'd be surprised.'

She looked at him questioningly, waiting for more, but that was all he said. She puzzled over what might unsettle his supreme confidence, but couldn't come up with anything, and in the end had to let it go.

The airport was small and the plane they were using a private one, so it took no time at all to pass through the checks. Shelby hugged her father at the departure gate.

'Please don't worry. I'll be fine,' she reassured him.

'I know you will, darling. Gray's a good man.'

She glanced round at Gray, who was standing just outside, carrying their luggage, which had been in the boot of the car. 'I guess that's why I love him so much,' she agreed softly, and saw the stunned expression that settled on her father's face. It was then that she realised she had spoken a little too loudly. Her secret was out.

'Shelby?' Oscar exclaimed, and she hastily stood on tip toe to kiss his cheek.

'Oh, Lord. I didn't mean to say that! It's a secret. Please, please, please don't tell him I said so because I don't think I've ever told him,' she pleaded, then gave him a crooked smile and hurried to join Gray.

Oscar Greer stood watching her in somewhat of a daze. Then he smiled, and the smile slowly broadened into a grin. He laughed, shaking his head in wonder and wry amusement. His gaze fell on Gray and his merriment deepened. Well, well, well, he thought, rubbing his hands together in glee. Who would have thought it? This couldn't have worked out better if he'd planned it himself.

Oblivious to it all, the two sources of his amusement were concentrating on each other.

'Everything OK?' Gray asked her as they walked towards a gleaming white jet.

'He's worried, but he knows I'll be fine,' she answered him distractedly, her attention on the aircraft. 'A Lear jet? You can't be serious!'

'Ever been on one?' he asked, and she shook her head, virtually speechless.

'I wish!'

That roguish smile twinkled down at her. 'Then you're in for the flight of your life,' he declared, helping her to mount the steps into the luxury jet. 'Sit anywhere you like. I'll just stow the luggage away.'

Shelby took a seat by the window and Gray had just joined her when the pilot walked through from the cockpit. He retracted the steps and locked the door before speaking to them.

Good morning, Mr Compton. Mr Ross sends his compliments. You'll find refreshments in the galley, and the rest room is just beyond that. We'll be taking off in a few minutes, and I hope you enjoy the flight.' With a respectful nod he went on his way and disappeared forward.

Shelby took an appreciative look around the luxurious interior. 'How do you know somebody who would lend you his Lear jet?'

Gray shrugged lightly. 'I got him out of a jam once and he's returning the favour.'

She was impressed. 'It must have been some jam!' she exclaimed ironically.

Gray merely smiled, and as the engines started at that moment, Shelby promptly forgot all about the mysterious Mr Ross. Having buckled herself in, she reached across and slipped her hand into Gray's. When he looked a question, her lips twitched.

'Flying makes you nervous, remember?'

Blue eyes gleamed back at her. 'So it does,' he responded, and tightened his grip.

Shelby felt her heart swell, and turned her attention to the world flashing by outside with a sigh of satisfaction. Now, if only she could get her memory back, life would be just about perfect.

CHAPTER EIGHT

THEY arrived at their final destination in the late afternoon. All Shelby knew was that they were in Scotland, and from the airport where they had landed Gray had driven them west in a hired Range Rover. The scenery was breathtaking and constantly changing as they travelled up the coast, then headed inland until finally he drew them to a halt before a house set on a hillside overlooking a loch.

A smiling woman came out of the house to meet them as they climbed out of the car.

'Mrs Menzies?' Gray queried, walking forward to shake hands.

'Aye. And you'll be Mr and Mrs Compton,' she confirmed in the lilting, softly spoken manner of the locals. Shelby shook hands, deciding there was no point in correcting the woman's error about their married state. 'Now, here are the keys. I've made up the bed for you and set the water heater. By the time you go to bed, there will be plenty of hot water. You'll find food in the refrigerator and logs for the fire are down in the cellar. It can get a wee bit chilly at night up here. If you need me for anything, you'll find me at the farm on the other side of the loch there.' She pointed to a collection of buildings in the near distance.

'Thank you, Mrs Menzies. You've been very kind,' Gray responded, taking the keys.

'You and your wife enjoy your stay, now,' Mrs Menzies declared with another friendly smile, then picked up a bicycle which had been hidden by the wall and rode off on it.

Shelby watched until the woman was out of sight, then

took a good deep breath of the fresh scented air. 'This is fantastic. How on earth did you find it?'

'Through a friend of a friend,' he answered vaguely.

'I never knew you had so many friends!' she declared, eyes dancing. 'Look at all those colours in the heather. Oh, I wish I had my sketch pad with me. I need to get this down on paper!' she exclaimed, receiving a sensory bombardment every way she looked.

Gray cast her a curious look out of those blue eyes. 'You paint?'

'One of the few things I inherited from my mother. I'm not a Turner or a Constable, but I get by,' she confirmed, sighing happily. 'You couldn't have chosen a better spot, I love it!'

'I don't want to dampen your enthusiasm, but we didn't pack any painting gear. We should be able to pick up a pad and some watercolours in the nearest town, though. Will that do?'

Shelby rubbed her hands together, enthused by the prospect of painting the myriad views. 'I can't wait.' Turning to him with a excited smile, she slipped her arms around his neck and sighed. 'Thank you for bringing me here,' she said huskily and, in a spontaneous gesture, raised herself on tiptoe to kiss him.

There was a fraction of a second when Gray didn't respond, but just when she was beginning to wonder at his reluctance his arms snaked round her, drawing her close. He took her simple thank you kiss and returned it with a searching one of his own. His teeth nipped at her lips, then his tongue soothed them with a silken glide. When she gasped at the tingle of pleasure, he took the opportunity to gain entry to the warm cavern of her mouth, searching out the sensitive spots with his tongue, urging her to meet him halfway, which she did with a sigh of satisfaction.

For mindless minutes they stood locked in each other's

arms, their kiss slowly but surely growing in passion until
the need for air caused Shelby to break the contact. 'Wow!'
she exclaimed with a husky laugh. 'What was that for?'

Gray's eyes only slowly lost their heated gleam. 'It's
been a long dry spell between kisses, and I couldn't resist
it any longer,' he confessed wryly and she smiled tenderly,
her hand cupping his cheek.

'I'm glad you didn't. We must have had a lot of practice,' she teased, and something flickered across his face
too quickly for her to interpret.

'Well, you know what they say, Red. Practice makes
perfect,' he joked back as he gently ran his hands up and
down her back.

'Mmm. In that case I'll definitely be finding out how
perfect you are later,' she flirted, only to frown when his
hands stopped their gentle stroking. 'What? What is it?'

'We shouldn't forget you were in an accident mere days
ago and only got out of hospital today. You don't want to
rush things,' he advised her, stepping back so that her arms
fell to her sides.

Not surprisingly, she looked at him oddly. He had ini-
tiated this, so why was he pulling back? 'The doctor said
I was in perfect health, except for the odd bruise or two.
I'm not an invalid.'

Gray's response was to ruffle her hair. 'I know you're
not, sweetheart, but it still hasn't been long.'

Shelby wasn't at all happy with that answer or the action.
'Don't you want to make love to me?' she demanded to
know, going straight to the heart of the matter, and Gray
uttered a dry laugh as he shook his head.

'Hell, Red, you have no idea! I want to do that so
damned much it hurts,' he told her gruffly, and there was
such a powerful look of desire in his eyes that she really
couldn't doubt his answer.

Moving closer, she placed her palms on his chest and

fluttered him a come-hither look. 'In that case there's nothing stopping you,' she declared alluringly.

Groaning, Gray placed his hands over hers, lest they threaten to stray enticingly. 'I only have so much control here, and you're enough to tempt a saint. Give me a break, Red. I'm trying to do what's right, which is give you time,' he added reasonably.

Her tongue peeped out to moisten her lips, causing him to catch his breath, which set her nerves jumping again. 'Thanks, but I don't want it,' she insisted and he closed his eyes for a moment.

'You've got it anyway.'

She stared at him in silence and with a lurch of her heart she thought she might have the real answer. 'There's something wrong with this relationship, isn't there? Something you're not telling me. That's why you're holding back,' she accused tightly, her heart starting to thump anxiously in her chest. Oh, God, could she have loved him and lost him all in the space of the weeks she couldn't remember? Was he just being kind until she did remember?

Gray looked at her for a long moment, then dragged a hand through his hair. 'There's nothing wrong between us, Red. Our relationship is as... strong as it ever was.'

As far as Shelby was concerned, he could be saying what she needed to hear rather than the truth. She had no way of knowing, and had never felt so vulnerable in her life. 'Is it? How do I know you're telling me the truth?' Her eyes were a little wild now and she was disastrously close to tears.

Swiftly taking her by the shoulders, Gray looked her squarely in the eye. 'Listen to me, Red. This is why I want to give you time, because your emotions are still recovering from the shock. Think. You have to know I wouldn't lie to you.'

Shelby held his gaze, reading the message he was trying

to send her. She had to believe he wouldn't lie or she was lost. She was overreacting, and it was all due to the accident—as he had told her.

Slumping against him, she rested her head on his chest and sighed. 'I'm sorry. It's just...not remembering us makes me nervous. Of course I believe you, Gray,' she said and felt his chest rise as he drew in air in a ragged sigh of his own.

'Thank you for that,' Gray responded gently, slipping an arm across her shoulders and starting them walking towards the house. 'Listen, darling, we're both a bit strained after all that's happened. That's why we're here. We need to relax and take things easy. How about we start with a hot cup of tea?'

Tea sounded just about perfect right then. 'Let's do a deal. I'll make us some tea whilst you bring the luggage in. How's that?' Shelby offered, raising her head to twinkle a smile up at him.

Laughing, Gray handed her the keys. 'I should have known you'd get out of the hard work somehow. Milk, no sugar,' he enlarged helpfully. Catching her chin in his hand, he held her steady whilst he dropped a kiss on her lips. 'Just a little something on account,' he grinned, then turned on his heel and headed back to the car.

Left to her own devices, Shelby went exploring. The house itself was old, but the interior had been improved to suit modern day needs. She found the kitchen easily enough, and set the kettle on to boil whilst she reconnoitred the rest of the ground floor. The sitting room was the cosiest she had ever seen, set about with rugs and comforters and deep-cushioned chairs and a settee just made to curl up in. On the upper floor there were four bedrooms, but only one ready for use. The main bedroom had an *en suite* bathroom and a spectacular view over the loch. As soon as she saw it, Shelby couldn't imagine sleeping anywhere else.

Humming cheerfully to herself, she jogged back downstairs and retraced her steps to the kitchen. With the tea brewing in the pot, she hunted through the cupboards for something to go with it and discovered a tin of home-made shortbread. It had to have been left there by Mrs Menzies, and Shelby made a note to thank her the next time she saw her.

They drank their tea in the garden, munching on melt-in-the-mouth shortbread whilst watching the world go by on the loch below. The bustle turned to a trickle and eventually died away as the sun slowly sank in the west, and it was only the first chill of evening which finally sent them inside.

Later they dined on soup with chunks of fresh bread and a fine red wine. Gray found an old movie channel on the television and Shelby curled up beside him on the settee, her head on his shoulder, an arm tucked behind him, her hand slipping beneath his shirt.

'This is nice.' She sighed comfortably. 'Do we do this often?'

'Not often enough,' he replied huskily, and shifted so that his arm was around her shoulders. 'Better?'

'Hmm, much,' she confirmed with a tiny sigh, a flirtatious smile hovering unseen about her lips. Slowly but surely her fingers began to trace lazy circles over his skin. For a while he appeared to ignore it, but then she felt the tension start to mount in him.

'Cut it out, Red,' he ordered gruffly, and her lips twitched.

'Cut what out?' she asked innocently, ignoring his command.

'You know what you're doing,' he countered, then gasped as her fingers found a particularly sensitive spot.

This time she laughed out loud. 'I most certainly do.'

Gray's hand found her chin and raised her head until

their eyes met. 'I give you fair warning, sweetheart. You're messing with the wrong man,' he growled.

Her eyes flirted with him recklessly. 'That's good!'

Swift as blinking, Shelby found herself lying on her back on the settee with Gray half leaning over her, his mouth twisted into a wolfish grin.

His teeth gleamed whitely as he said, 'You're playing a dangerous game.'

'It's the only type worth playing,' Shelby flirted wickedly. She might not recall how they had come to be lovers, but flirting with him like this felt as right and comfortable as an old pair of shoes—only far more exciting.

'You know, there are two ways this can go,' he informed her, insinuating his hand beneath her T-shirt, causing her to catch her breath this time.

'Is that so?' she murmured breathlessly, her pulse beginning to trip faster in her ears.

His fingers glided upwards until they brushed the lower slopes of her breasts. His voice became huskily sensual. 'I could kiss you, or...'

Her eyes widened expectantly. 'Or...?'

'I could simply do this,' he went on in an altogether different tone and, before she could stop him, he began to tickle her ruthlessly.

'No!' Shelby exclaimed before she was overcome by tickle-induced laughter. She bucked, writhed and squirmed, all to no avail. Gray was stronger than she was and he knew just where to tickle her to undermine her best efforts at escape. One of her flailing arms caught him around the ear and, to avoid getting hit again, he buried his head in her neck. Just as it got to the point where it was hurting her to laugh, he stopped, raising his head to look down at her.

'Had enough?'

'H-hardly,' she puffed. 'I'm just getting my second wind!'

Laughing, Gray rested his weight on his elbows and looked at her admiringly. 'I'll say this for you, Shelby Greer. You're a real terrier when it comes to defending yourself.'

Shelby was beginning to get her breath back now. 'That had better be a compliment.'

The look in his eyes softened. 'It was.'

She let out a sighing breath. 'I wanted you to kiss me,' she told him with a faint pout and he smoothed it out with the brush of his thumb, sending a tingling throughout her body.

'I know,' he replied softly. 'To tell you the truth, Red. I could keep on kissing you from now until for ever and never get tired of it. That isn't the problem.'

'Then what is the problem?' she asked him, her heart melting.

Removing his thumb, he replaced it with his lips, gently rubbing, nipping and teasing with teeth and tongue. 'If I get started, I won't want to stop.'

Shelby's lids fluttered down over her eyes as she sought to return each caress. 'Me neither.'

Her lips parted and he breached her defences, searching out her tongue with his own, enticing her to join him, which she did gladly. He groaned deep in his throat.

'You're so damned addictive. I want you so much, it's driving me crazy.' The powerful words were enough to ignite their mutual passion, which was never far from the surface.

Shelby cradled the back of his head with her hand and gave herself up to the infinite pleasure of kissing him. She knew how he felt, for she felt it too. As the kiss deepened, became more and more arousing, her whole body thrummed with need. Kiss followed kiss, each wilder and more passionate than the last, and she moaned, wanting more, needing him to touch her. As if he could read her mind, Gray's hand once more slid beneath her T-shirt, but this time to caress, not to tease. As he sought out her breast, she arched into his touch, gasping at the shaft of pleasure that swept through her.

This, she thought, as her hands clung on to him, was what she was born for. To be with him. To experience everything with him. It felt so gloriously, wonderfully right, that she wanted it to go on for ever. Yet, even as she thought it, she could sense Gray drawing back. She knew it wasn't easy for him to break free of the passion which threatened to overwhelm them, yet he did it, pulling back so that once more he was looking down at her, but this time the coals of desire still burned in his eyes and he was breathing hard.

'You see what I mean?' he growled. 'Every time it gets harder and harder to call a halt.'

'But I told you it wasn't necessary,' she reminded him.

With a deep sigh, Gray pushed himself up and away from her, combing faintly trembling hands through his hair. 'I know, but I have rules, Red, and one of them is not to take advantage of the situation.' It would help a great deal if she didn't keep trying to seduce him.

'I'm starting to hate rules.' She sighed as she too sat up and restored her clothes to a semblance of order. 'Tell me how we came to get together, instead,' she compromised, settling herself back beside him.

'Shouldn't you be remembering that on your own?'

'Probably,' she agreed with a grimace. 'But what if I never remember? I want to know, Gray.' She looked up at him, green eyes large and pleading.

Caught in their spell, he knew he had to say something, even if it did blow up in his face later. It wouldn't be the truth, but it could have been, had luck been on his side. And there was always the chance that one small seed could fall on fertile ground. He was taking so many risks, what did one more matter?

So, making himself comfortable, he drew her close. 'It was after one of those dinners at your father's, just after I returned from Japan. We were having one of our customary exchanges of words. You accused me yet again of playing games with you, and my patience finally snapped. I told you how wrong you were, that I'd wanted you for years, and that if you'd ever bothered to ask me my side of the story, things might be different between us.'

It sounded entirely plausible to Shelby, recalling how convinced she had been of his guilt. She had refused to listen. 'What did I say to that?'

'You were lost for words to start with. A miracle in itself. After a moment you demanded I explain what I meant,' he told her, glancing down to see how she was taking it, and saw her bite her lip.

For her part, Shelby could picture herself with her arms crossed defensively, glaring at him so he shouldn't see her consternation. When you'd been hurt you wouldn't easily be won over, even if you longed to be. 'What did you do then?'

A nerve ticked in his jaw as he answered. 'Like I told you the other day, I explained that, whilst Oscar had asked me, I had refused. The reason I sought you out was because I wanted to. I'd waited long enough.'

That had her sitting up and looking at him. 'So how come you pushed me away when we were out on the terrace, and said you weren't attracted to me?' she challenged him.

He smiled ruefully, though his gaze was watchful. 'Exactly what you asked me the last time we had this conversation, and the answer is still the same. I lied.'

'You lied?' she charged incredulously, and Gray shrugged.

'You had had too much to drink,' he was swift to point out, and Shelby rolled her eyes helplessly.

'Of course I had. To bolster my courage. I'd never tried to seduce you before!'

One eyebrow quirked. 'Really? I didn't know you'd needed Dutch courage. I always imagined you had the gall to do anything.'

Not where he was concerned. Her heart was involved, and that changed everything. 'Yes, well… For your information, I'm not the hussy you take me for.'

He smiled faintly. 'If I thought anything about you, Red, it was that you were the most alluring woman I had ever met. You still are.'

One look at his face told her he wasn't joking, and it did her heart a power of good. It wasn't that she was expecting him to declare he loved her. She was too sensible for that. However, she could begin to hope that this attraction between them would not easily be satisfied. Having accepted they had a relationship, time was what she needed now. Time to make memories. Then, when it was all finally over, she could open up the secret place in her heart and warm herself on the old flames. However, that was ahead of her. She had to concentrate on now.

'So it's true what they say: third time's the charm. Here we are, together at last. Who would have thought it? What will become of us, do you think?'

He smiled, eyes searching hers for something she couldn't tell if he found or not. 'Time will tell, sweetheart. Time will most surely tell.'

Suddenly the future was full of unknown possibilities, and she was glad she hadn't given in to doubt. 'Let's go to bed,' she suggested, then, seeing the look on his face, laughed huskily. 'I didn't mean that. I'm tired.'

Gray rose at once and helped her to her feet. 'You go

on up whilst I check everything's secure down here. I've put your bags in the main bedroom.'

'Don't be long,' she urged him as she headed for the stairs.

'I won't be,' he promised.

Up in the master bedroom, Shelby decided against drawing the curtains as there was hardly likely to be anyone looking in, they were so isolated. Looking at the comfortable bed, she was suddenly aware of just how tired she was. It had been a long day, mostly spent travelling. Much as she would like to have clambered into the bed as she was, she rummaged in her case for her wash bag, a towel and her night things, and took them into the *en suite* bathroom.

The shower was blissfully warm and she was tempted to stay under it. Yet she had no idea just how much hot water there was so, after washing, she stepped out and dried herself off, slipping into a blue silk nightie. Towel-drying her hair, she wandered back into the bedroom, and it was only then that she noticed that Gray's bags were missing. The towel dropped to the floor as she crossed to the fitted wardrobe on the off-chance he had unpacked his things already. It took but a moment to discover that the wardrobe and dressers were empty.

Then she heard the sound of a door closing and followed the sound to the room opposite. Gray must have come up whilst she was in the shower, for he was in the process of unpacking his clothes in that room. Standing in the doorway watching, her heart sank.

'What's going on?' she asked abruptly, causing him to glance round.

He straightened with a small stack of clothes in his hand. 'I thought I'd sleep in this room,' Gray informed her evenly. 'Just until you're healed.'

'I am healed,' Shelby told him tautly. 'There's no reason

for you to sleep anywhere else—unless you don't want to sleep with me. Is that what you're really trying to say?'

Gray dropped the clothes back into his bag and rubbed a weary hand around his neck. After a moment he sighed and shook his head. 'No, that isn't what I'm trying to say at all. Shelby, this whole situation is complicated enough without adding more pressure.'

A tiny bubble of anger started to expand in her chest. 'The situation wouldn't be complicated at all if you started acting naturally. We're lovers. What could be more natural than us sleeping in the same bed?'

Gray settled his hands on his hips and stared at her hard, a nerve ticking away in his jaw. 'I've already told you I'm trying to do the right thing.'

Down by her sides, Shelby's hands curled into fists. 'I don't want the right thing, I want you. Sleeping beside me in our bed! If you're worried about me pouncing on you, don't be. I've already accepted that we're going to wait.'

His chest rose and fell as he drew in a long breath. 'Did it ever occur to you that I might be worried about me pouncing on you?'

She folded her arms at that. 'Don't be silly. You wouldn't!'

Her confidence had his brows lifting. 'Oh, wouldn't I?'

'No,' Shelby declared emphatically. 'No matter what the provocation, you'd never do anything like that.'

Gray closed his eyes and gave his head a swift shake as if to clear it, then he laughed wryly. 'Thanks for the vote of confidence, but it changes nothing.'

Shelby narrowed her eyes on him. 'You're determined to sleep here?'

'For tonight,' he confirmed.

'Oh!' she muttered direly and, spinning on her heel, marched out of the room.

After a moment or two Gray returned to his unpacking,

but he was hardly any further forward when Shelby marched back into the room, a pillow clutched in her hand. Giving him a fiery look, she walked round him, tossed her pillow on to the bare mattress, followed on after it and made herself comfortable on her side with her back to him.

'What do you think you're doing?' Gray asked shortly, and she answered without looking at him.

'If Mohammed won't go to the mountain, the mountain must go to Mohammed!'

'You can't possibly sleep here like that!' he argued, and saw her shrug.

'If you can, I can.'

There followed a moment of fraught silence where all that could be heard was the gnashing of Gray's teeth.

'There are two other bedrooms in this house,' he declared finally and at that she did glance over her shoulder at him.

'I'll follow you wherever you go. I intend to sleep with you, Gray, so you'd better make your mind up to it,' she advised him, turning back and struggling to find a cosy position.

Maybe it was a stupid stand to take, but to Shelby it was important. She wanted to be close to him. Needed it, for she didn't remember any of the closeness that they must have shared. All she wanted was to lie in his arms and go to sleep. That wasn't too much to ask, was it?

The next thing she knew, two arms were slipping beneath her, lifting her up. With a cry, she began to struggle.

'Quit that,' Gray ordered as he strode with his belligerent armful into the master bedroom. He fell short of dumping her unceremoniously on the bed, setting her down gently in view of her recent accident. Immediately he released her, though, Shelby made a bid to scramble off the bed on the other side.

Gray had to dive across the bed and catch her arm.

Shelby stared him out. 'Stay where you are, damn it!' he growled angrily.

Shelby froze, but remained poised for action. 'I'm not going to sleep here on my own!' she told him bluntly, which received a snort of dry amusement from Gray.

'You won't be. You've won,' he told her shortly. Releasing her he strode from the room and, as she blinked rapidly in amazement at her victory, then hastily slipped beneath the covers, she could hear him moving about.

Seconds later he came back in with her pillow under one arm and holding his bag in the other. He kicked the door shut, dropped the bag on the floor and tossed the pillow in her general direction.

'Don't say another word,' he ordered, stabbing a finger towards her. 'Or, so help me God, I'll give you the spanking you never got as a child!'

Shelby clutched the pillow to her chest and watched him. He put away his clothes with the minimum of effort, gathered together what he would need for the night, and disappeared into the bathroom. Her breath escaped on a tiny sigh then. Maybe she had gone a little too far, she thought regretfully. She hadn't wanted to make him angry. She just wanted to be near him.

Sighing again, she put the pillow beneath her head and waited. Ten minutes later, dressed only in a pair of shorts, Gray returned, snapping off the bathroom light and then the bedroom light as he went. Shelby caught the merest glimpse of supple tanned male flesh before the room was plunged into darkness and he slipped into the bed beside her. She lay quiet, the gap between them seeming as large as an ocean.

Suddenly the bed rocked as Gray moved closer. Then a long arm reached out, pulling her into his side.

'Neither of us will get any sleep with you over there and me over here,' he growled huskily and a wave of relief swept through Shelby, bringing a smile of happiness to her lips.

Without a word, she curled up against him, resting her head on his shoulder, her hand placed over his heart. Minutes later, she was asleep.

Sensing it, Gray laid his arm across his eyes and prayed for the same to happen to him. Yet inside he knew that the desired sleep was going to be a long time coming.

CHAPTER NINE

WHEN Shelby awoke next morning she was alone in the bed. Reaching out to run her hand over the place where Gray had slept, she found it cool, proving he had been gone some time. Stretching with that particularly feline type of feminine pleasure, she felt refreshed, full of energy for the day ahead.

She wondered where Gray was. Though she listened hard, she could hear no sounds coming from downstairs. Throwing back the covers, she rose and padded over to the window. For a moment or two the spectacular view claimed all her attention, but then she caught some movement out of the corner of her eye and glanced down.

Gray was steadily jogging up the road towards the house. When he reached the car he stopped, and Shelby was impressed by the fact that he was hardly puffing at all. Right now he was wearing a khaki coloured vest, black shorts and running shoes. He looked handsome and rugged and set her senses tingling in no time at all.

Opening the window, she leant out. 'Good morning,' she called brightly, and he turned, looking up at her with hands on hips. 'Isn't it an absolutely glorious day? Why didn't you wake me?'

'You looked too peaceful,' Gray answered. 'Besides, I didn't think you were into jogging.'

She laughed. 'I'm not, but I would have enjoyed watching you. Did you know you've got really sexy legs?'

He grinned back at her. 'Come down here and tell me again,' he ordered, and she gave him a wary look.

'I don't know if I should. You look a bit dangerous!'

'All the more reason to come, then,' Gray returned, flashing that roguish smile of his and sending tingles down her spine.

'Well, seeing as you put it like that...' Shelby said, laughing, and left the window to go in search of her clothes.

Less than ten minutes later, having washed and dressed in shorts, top and trainers, she tripped down the stairs and went in search of him. She found him eventually, leaning against the fence that marked the boundary of the garden, talking on his mobile phone. He beckoned her over and, as she drew closer, she could hear his side of the conversation.

'It was who we thought, then? Which station? Let's hope they throw away the key... My pleasure, Oscar, and I hereby notify you I'm taking a long leave of absence.'

Shelby's ears perked up at that. 'Hey, are you talking to Dad?' she asked, and Gray nodded, holding out his hand for her to come closer.

'Yes, that's Shelby you can hear. She finally decided to get up. I think she wants to talk to you. Hold on.' He handed over his phone, then slipped his arms around her.

'Hi, Dad,' she greeted her father cheerfully, resting her weight against Gray.

'Hello, darling. You sound more chipper today. Feeling better?'

'Much. It's probably got something to do with the company,' she added, winking at Gray, who quirked an eyebrow back at her.

Oscar Greer laughed. 'Of course it has. I remember how it felt to be with the right person. Nothing to compare with it. You take care now, and enjoy yourself. Oh, and tell Gray something for me. Faint heart never won anything.'

Shelby frowned, more than a little confused by that. 'OK, I will. Bye, Dad, See you soon.' Closing the phone down, she handed it back to Gray, who slipped it into the pocket of his shorts. 'Dad said to tell you faint heart never won anything. Do you understand that?'

'It's a private joke,' he responded inscrutably.

'Yes, but what does it mean?' she insisted.

'I'll tell you one day,' he told her unhelpfully. 'Now, what were you saying about my legs?'

Her smile broadened into a grin. 'I like a man with long legs. They're very sexy.'

He grinned back at her, and there was a rakish gleam in his eye. 'Mmm. I was just thinking the same thing about you. I've been imagining you wrapping them around me when I make love to you,' Gray added huskily, and a powerful wave of heat started in the pit of her stomach and swept through her entire body.

Shelby made a growling sound. 'I love it when you say things like that. Tell me more.'

'Do you really feel better today?' he asked instead, and the prosaic question made her tut.

'Much. Why?'

Gray lowered his head towards hers. 'Because I'm badly in need of sustenance. I've been starving for your kisses for far too long.'

The tone and texture of his words caused Shelby to shiver in anticipation. 'Then you'd better not waste time talking,' she invited, and he needed no further encouragement.

Gray took her lips with a depth of need that blew her mind. Of the kisses she could remember, nothing compared to this. It might have been shocking if she hadn't felt an equal hunger. He sought and she gave, revelling in the release of his pent up passion. She had wanted him to kiss her like this, and it gave her the freedom to kiss him back without reservation.

When they finally broke the kiss, her heart was thundering wildly and she could scarcely breathe. Yet it felt wonderful, for beneath her hand she could feel the rapid thud of his heart and could see the way he had to drag air into his lungs.

Gray rested his forehead against hers and strove for a measure of calm. 'Now do you see why I had to hold back?' he asked thickly, and her nerves responded instantly.

Oh, yes, she saw. 'Is it always going to be like this?'

'What do you think? My passion for you can never be moderate,' he confessed in a husky growl her senses instantly responded to.

'I'm glad we got over the past. Think what we would be missing. Do you feel foolish for turning me down all those years ago?' she just had to ask, but he shook his head.

'No. It wasn't the right time. You had a lot of growing up to do.'

Naturally she frowned at that. 'Oh, I did, did I? What makes you think I didn't know my own mind?'

'Oh, you knew your own mind, all right. Which is why you were having so much fun playing the field,' Gray responded, and she knew she only had herself to blame for his thinking. She had covered her tracks well.

'Maybe you're right,' she conceded. One day, if their relationship should turn out to be more than an affair, she would tell him the truth.

At that point her stomach growled, and Gray released her. 'Come on, Red. Let's drive into town for breakfast. Then we'll buy your painting equipment and drive up into the mountains.'

'That sounds like a wonderful idea,' Shelby agreed instantly.

Fifteen minutes later they were in the car and on their way. It turned out to be the most perfect day she could ever remember. After a lazy breakfast, having found the things she needed, they stopped off to buy a picnic lunch then headed inland. Everywhere they looked was a feast for the eyes. They were so spoilt for choice that in the end Gray simply parked the car and they walked.

Whenever Shelby saw something she just had to sketch they would stop. Whilst she painted, Gray stretched out beside her. Sometimes he would watch her work, and at others he closed his eyes and dozed.

By mid-afternoon Shelby was beginning to feel hungry again. Gray found them a sheltered spot, miles from anywhere, and spread out the blanket he had carried from the car. Here they could eat and look at the stunning view at the same time.

Some time later, Shelby sighed. 'I should have done this a long time ago. I've been so busy focusing on my career I'd forgotten what it feels like to really relax.'

'So the knock on the head saved someone having to knock you on the head to get you to take a holiday?' Gray teased lightly, and she threw the crust of her sandwich at him.

Taking two plums from a bag, he handed her one, then lay down and made himself comfortable with his head on her lap. Shelby leant back against a convenient outcrop of granite and slowly ate her plum, and all the while her fingers idly combed through his silky black hair.

'Oh-oh. You've got a grey hair!' she exclaimed, tossing the stone of her plum back into the bag.

'I'm surprised there's only one,' Gray replied dryly, handing her his plum stone to deal with. 'The amount of worry you give me, there should be more.'

'When have you ever worried over me?' Shelby wanted to know, putting the plum stone in the bag along with her own.

Gray captured her hand on its way back to his hair. 'More times than I care to remember.' One by one he began to lick her fingers clean of plum juice.

Shelby caught her breath at the sensuousness of it. 'Are

you sure you want to be doing that?' she asked, finding it highly arousing. 'It's giving me ideas.'

'I hoped it might,' he responded, moving his tongue in lazy spirals round her index finger.

'I'm shocked!' she gasped, stifling a groan of pleasure. He was turning her on as easily as if he had flicked a switch.

Gray abandoned her fingers in favour of tracing lazy circles around her palm with his tongue. 'Brace yourself, Red. You ain't seen nothing yet,' he promised.

'You always seem such a gentleman,' she retorted, biting her lip as his tongue discovered the pulse at her wrist.

He looked up at her then, eyes gleaming hotly. 'You bring out the beast in me!'

Her smile at that was a study in provocation. 'Thank God. I thought I might be losing my touch.'

Gray shook his head. 'That will never happen between you and me. You only have to touch me and I go up in flames.'

It was an opportunity not to be missed, and Shelby swiftly bent down and kissed him. She took her time, tasting his lips before slipping her tongue inside and wreaking her own brand of sensual havoc. When she was done, she raised her head just enough to see him. 'Like that?' she asked softly.

He smiled wickedly, deliberately misunderstanding. 'I liked it so much you can do it again.' Raising his hand, he curled it around her nape and urged her head down.

This time the kiss was mutual and all the more potent for it. The more time they took, the swifter was her body's response. Her heart had quickened its beat, sending her blood pulsing thickly through her veins. Every nerve was aroused, aching for more.

'Gray?' His name was an aching plea against his lips and drew an immediate response.

'Yes,' he confirmed tautly, moving so that she was lying down and he was bending over her.

The weight of his body resting on hers was an indescribable pleasure. Her breasts swelled in response, her nipples hardening to sensual points that craved to be touched. When one hard male thigh slid between hers, she uttered a moan of pleasure and arched against it instinctively. Her hands sought to touch him wherever she could, tangling in his hair one moment, tugging at his T-shirt the next so that she could explore the tanned flesh beneath it.

It was incredibly satisfying to feel him shiver beneath her touch. To know that she could affect him so strongly. When his hand slipped beneath her top in search of her breasts she could hardly bear the suspense of waiting, and when his fingers finally brushed the lacy bra aside and claimed her aching flesh he felt it in every inch of her body. He subjected her to the most delicious torment, teasing her with lazy circles of his thumb until she wanted to scream. Then and only then did he take the time to swiftly remove her top and bra and claim the turgid peak with his mouth.

Her head went back as his tongue laved her sensitive flesh, teasing her with flickering strokes that stole her breath until at last he began to suckle, drawing her deep into his mouth until she groaned deep in her throat at the pure unadulterated pleasure. Then he began to repeat the process on her other breast, and she was helpless to do anything other than close her eyes and succumb. Yet eventually that was not enough. She wanted to touch him, to make him feel what she was feeling, and she began tugging at his T-shirt, pulling it up until Gray was forced to stop what he was doing and raise himself enough to allow her to pull the top free and toss it aside.

Their eyes locked then and oh, so slowly he lowered himself until their skin touched. It was an instant of pure pleasure that stole their breath and left them, for vital aeons, not daring to move. Shelby breathed in deeply, her arms gliding around his neck.

'Mmm, that feels so good,' she murmured huskily.

'Almost too good,' Gray agreed, tracing a line of kisses along the tender lines of her shoulder and neck. His hand made a slow exploration down the curve of her waist, only to be frustrated by her shorts. 'You're wearing too much,' he growled, nimbly dealing with the button and zip.

'So are you,' she pointed out, and he moved.

'That can soon be put right.'

Shelby raised her hips to allow him to remove the last of her clothes and then he dealt with his own. Seconds later he lay down again and, with nothing between them, everywhere they touched flash-fires started to blaze. The freedom to explore was intoxicating, the pleasure given and received beyond anything either had experienced before. It was hard to tell where one body ended and the other began as they writhed together, each kiss and caress drawing gasps and sighs of pleasure as they drove each other closer to the edge.

When his hand found her intimately and began a stroking caress, it was so overwhelmingly erotic that Shelby could feel her body tighten, the pressure rapidly building and spiralling upwards towards the inevitable.

'No. Wait,' she gasped urgently, but it was already too late. She had no power to hold back an explosive climax that had her arching into his hand and crying out. The waves of pleasure pulsed through her as she collapsed, and conflicting emotions surged through her. As much as she had enjoyed the release, it wasn't how she had wanted it to be. She had wanted them to come together.

Sensing her disappointment, Gray settled himself between her legs, taking his weight on his arms as he looked down at her flushed cheeks and glittering eyes. 'That's only the beginning, darling. Stay with me,' he urged and with infinite care he began to arouse her again.

Shelby knew he was right when within minutes she could feel her body starting to turn molten again. Her desire had only died back, not been put out, and soon it was a growing fire in the pit of her stomach. Determined that he should not get off scot-free, she used her lips and hands to caress him wherever she could reach, and it was highly arousing to hear him gasp beneath her touch and shudder with the pleasure.

When he entered her she was ready for him, and it was the most beautiful moment of her life. He didn't just fill her physically, he filled her emotionally too. He completed her, for in her heart they were two halves of a whole. Only in these precious moments was she totally whole. She wanted to capture the moment in her memory for all time, but when he started to move thoughts flew from her mind and there was only feeling.

Folding her legs around him, she held on, moving to meet his thrusts. They were slow at first, measured by the strength of his control, but as need grew she could feel his control slipping away, until finally he abandoned it altogether in the search for mutual satisfaction. It came in a white-hot explosion that shattered her first and then Gray. They cried out at the sheer perfection of the moment.

Tears sparkled like diamonds in her eyes as she slowly floated back down to earth. Nothing could really have prepared her for what she felt then. The tears were of joy, for she knew that this was what she had dreamed of for so long. Gray was hers, and she was for ever his. Nothing could ever replace this. She wouldn't even try.

Gray somehow found the strength to roll on to his side, his chest rising and falling rapidly as he strove for breath. Turning his head, he looked at her and something knifed through him as he saw one perfect tear trickle from the corner of her eye.

'Hey. Are you all right, Red?' he asked, concern making his voice raspy.

Her response was to turn on her side to face him, her lips curving into a beatific smile. 'I'm perfectly fine,' she told him, searching his eyes for any signs of how he felt now.

'Why the tear?' Gray wanted to know, using a long finger to wipe the moisture away.

She sighed, so replete she felt as if she was lying on cotton wool, not a rough blanket. 'Because that was so beautiful. Wasn't it?'

His hand cupped her cheek, and at last he smiled rather bemusedly. 'It was surely way beyond my expectations. I always knew that you and I could have something special.'

The words surprised her. 'Isn't it always like that?' she asked, and Gray went still before uttering an odd laugh.

'Trust me, Red. What we just shared was one of a kind,' he assured her swiftly.

Shelby looked at him soberly. 'I have to trust you. You're the only one with a link to what I can't remember.'

Very gently he rubbed his thumb over her lips. 'Hey, forget what you can't remember. What we just shared is what counts. It has to mean something.'

'Perhaps it means we love each other,' she suggested, knowing that that was what she would like it to mean, but Gray could have other ideas. She had no reason for thinking his feelings towards her were anything more than physical.

An odd gleam shone from the back of his eyes. 'Perhaps it does,' he agreed lazily.

As an answer it left a lot to be desired, but she pursued it. 'Are we in love?'

'What do you think?' he countered, and his voice took on a husky edge.

She frowned at him, hard. 'Do you have any idea how aggravating it is to have your question answered with a question?'

His smile was roguish. 'I've a pretty good idea.'

Shelby narrowed her eyes at him. 'You're avoiding the question!'

'Yes,' he admitted at once, and she sighed helplessly.

'OK, so I have to make my own deduction. We're not in love, and you don't want to tell me because you don't want to hurt my feelings by telling me before I remember for myself. Right?'

'Wrong,' he batted back instantly, and Shelby's heart did an almighty flip-flop in her chest as his answer registered.

'Are you…' she began croakily, then had to stop to moisten her mouth. 'Are you telling me we do love each other?' she asked incredulously.

'Not exactly. It would be truer to say one of us loves the other,' he enlarged, moving closer to her.

The bottom of her stomach dropped out. Oh, God, did he mean he knew she loved him? It would be excruciatingly embarrassing if he felt nothing for her but, having come so far on an idle remark, she had to go on.

'Meaning…?'

Sapphire eyes looked directly into hers. 'Meaning I love you,' he said simply, and she lay there, stunned.

'You do?' She couldn't help the question sounding so doubtful, but it was the last thing she had expected him to say.

'As God is my witness. I love you, Shelby Greer. I'm hoping that maybe you love me too.' His words as well as his expression reflected hope muted by doubt. It was this uncertainty that convinced her he really wasn't joking.

Her spirits suddenly soared as it dawned on her that her wildest dream had just been answered. Love shone from her like a beacon. 'But of course I love you, Gray. I always have!'

It was his turn to show surprise. 'Always?'

Laughing, she nodded. 'Yes. Always.'

'Hmm, as I recall, you weren't too enamoured of me for a while,' he reminded her.

'True, but even though I hated you for what I thought you'd done, I loved you too,' she admitted, causing his smile to turn wolfish.

'I'd never have guessed. Remind me never to play poker with you,' he declared, running his hand caressingly over her hip, inflaming senses that had barely died down.

Shelby inched closer till their lips were a mere breath apart. 'Keep that up, mister, and you'll have to pay the consequences,' she warned him, letting her own fingers trail down his chest until they found a flat male nipple which they began to tease into a hard nub.

Gray's arm snaked around her waist, holding her to him as he rolled so that she lay atop him, her legs straddling his hips. 'Do your worst, Red. I've been dreaming of what it might be for a long time.'

With a husky laugh she took him at his word, using her hands, lips and tongue to explore her way down his firm male body. Gray allowed her free rein, and it was highly arousing to Shelby to hear his moans and feel the results of her caresses in his involuntary movements. When she found his aroused flesh and closed her fingers around the velvety shaft, he jerked wildly, hips leaving the ground as if he had just been given an electric shock.

'Hell's teeth!' he growled tautly, breathing fast, then groaned deeply as she let her fingers slide up and down with excruciating slowness.

Sensing that it was taking all his control to lie still and allow her this freedom, Shelby took pity on him. Rising, she settled herself over his hips and lowered herself on to him until he was deep inside her. Only then did she begin to move, rocking her hips rhythmically, rising and falling, intent on slowly stoking the fire that was growing inside them. Yet Gray had other plans. His hands trailed from her hips up to her breasts, teasing her nipples into aching peaks, then snaked down again to seek out the hub of her passion. The sensual stroking shattered her control and sent the throbbing coils of desire spiralling upwards towards release. She fell forwards and he caught her, rolling so that he was on top again, and with powerful thrusts of his hips he drove them both over the edge a second time.

When he had recovered enough to move, Gray eased his weight off her but kept his arm around her.

'How was it for you?' he asked with a faint laugh, and Shelby answered with a groan.

'Pretty spectacular, actually. Was it my imagination or did fireworks go off?' Making love with him was an experience she could never have imagined. None of her dreams had brought her anywhere close to the reality.

'I think it was a twenty gun salute,' he returned wryly.

Shelby blinked up at the clear blue sky. 'I can't move,' she said happily. 'You should carry a government health warning. Making love with this man seriously damages your strength!'

Laughing, Gray sat up, bringing her with him, and began reaching for their clothes. 'Much as I would like to stay here with you all day, it's going to get colder pretty soon. We'd better cut along back to the house.'

Reluctantly, Shelby slipped back into her clothes. She had wanted the moment to last for ever, but knew he was right. There was nothing in the least romantic about being up on a mountain when the sun went down.

When she was dressed, Gray held out a hand and pulled her to her feet and into his arms.

'You were worth waiting for, Red. No regrets?' he asked,

eyes searching hers with a sudden intensity she couldn't explain.

'None,' she responded at once. 'I love you.'

His smile didn't appear and his expression remained serious. 'I love you too. Remember that.'

Shelby frowned. 'Why would I forget?' she asked, and he sighed heavily.

'We none of us know what's round the corner,' he replied mysteriously, releasing her to pick up their belongings.

Shelby puzzled over what he had said as they made their way back down to where they had left the car, but had to give it up as a bad job. Whatever he meant was doomed to remain a mystery, for she couldn't foresee any reason why she would forget. Besides, she had other things to think about, such as the fact that, against all the odds, they loved each other.

One day she would want to know how and when he had fallen in love with her and why he had taken so long to tell her. However, for now, just knowing it was enough. For the first time since her accident, the future didn't seem so scary.

CHAPTER TEN

THERE were times in the next few days when Shelby had to give herself a pinch in order to convince herself she wasn't dreaming. She was so happy that half the time she felt as if she were walking on air. She had never seen Gray so relaxed. It was wonderful being with him. The days were a joy, the nights a revelation.

There was a quality to their lovemaking that she had never felt before, and she knew it was because she loved him. Love gave everything they said and did a different nuance. She couldn't have explained it in words; she just knew it was there because of her feelings for Gray and his for her. Life had never been more perfect.

Towards the end of the week, Gray decided to drive into the village to pick up some much needed groceries. Shelby opted to stay behind to do some washing. They had got through most of the clothes they had brought with them. It brought a smile to her lips as she set a load on to wash, remembering just how some of the clothes had got grubby. Humming to herself, she went upstairs to change the sheets and see if there was anything else that needed freshening.

The bed having been stripped and remade, she glanced round for anything she had missed. There was a towel and some other items of clothing draped over the chair in the corner of the bedroom and it was as she gathered them up that something fell off on to the floor. Glancing down in surprise, Shelby discovered it was Gray's wallet and he would need it to pay for the groceries. Tossing the washing on to the bed, she reached down for the leather case. It had fallen open and she realised, as she picked it up, that the reason it didn't close properly was because he kept a folded-up handkerchief in it.

Shelby hadn't intended to pry but her curiosity was piqued. Unfolding the linen square, to her surprise she found a smudge of lipstick on it. Her brows rose. Why on earth was he keeping a dirty handkerchief in his wallet? The answer swiftly followed the question. She hadn't considered Gray to be an overly sentimental man, but the handkerchief and its smudge had to mean something to him.

She couldn't exactly say why, but her heart lurched anxiously. The happiness she had been feeling faded away as she slowly folded the linen back as she had found it. She was about to replace it when the corner of a photograph caught her attention next. Gray had shown her a photograph before, and she wondered if this was it. She was sure he wouldn't mind her taking another look.

Easing the photo out, she took it across to the window for a better look. Yes, it was the same one. As she angled it, sunlight caught on something outside the window and reflected it back into the room, blinding her temporarily. Pain shot through her head and she winced, pressing a hand to her temple. Whatever the flash had been, it left her with a nagging background headache.

Doing her best to ignore it, Shelby examined the photo again. She smiled. Apart from the incident in the toilet, it had been a great evening. There had been a photographer doing the rounds of the tables, taking snaps. She hadn't realised he'd kept this one...

Her breath caught in her throat as she realised what she was thinking. She could remember this photograph being taken, and that could only mean one thing. She had got her memory back. There was a seat built into the window embrasure and she dropped on to it, probing her brain for the hitherto elusive memories. They all came flooding back as the gates were opened. The threats. Gray. The accident.

Some things were a little fuzzy, but basically she recalled everything.

Including the events after the accident.

It was as if a fist had fastened on her heart. She stared at the picture, feeling sick. There was no 'us'. This wasn't a photo of the two of them together because they were in love with each other. It was all lies! Everything he had told her in the hospital had been a lie, and that meant these last few days had been pure fabrication too.

Shelby pressed a hand to her mouth. Oh, dear God. She had told him she loved him. He had said he loved her too. Yet how could he? They had been attracted to each other, but it wasn't love—for him. Everything was suddenly very clear. He had invented that because of her accident. He had needed to keep her safe, and he had needed to be with her. The best way to accomplish that was to say they were lovers already.

Her head swam with the enormity of it, and she was hit by an intense wave of hurt. He had lied and she had believed it. She would have gone on believing it, had her memory not returned by looking at the photo he had left behind with his wallet when he'd gone out.

Her head came up at that, alerting her to a new fact. Gray had gone out. He had gone out and left her here. Alone. The one thing he had been careful not to do. Which could only mean the situation had changed. There was only one thing which could do that. The man had been found. He was no longer a threat. Of course it was a relief to know she was out of danger, but it couldn't alter the fact that the world she had believed to be so perfect had just collapsed around her like a house of cards!

The creak of a board caused her to look round and her heart lurched painfully when she saw Gray standing in the doorway. His eyes went from her stricken face to the washing, his wallet and then the photo she still held, assessing the situation in an instant. He took a deep breath, his expression becoming watchful.

'I forgot my wallet,' he told her simply, and Shelby nodded. It was probably the sunlight flashing off something on the car that had triggered the whole thing off.

'I found it in the washing and thought you wouldn't mind my looking at our photo again,' she said flatly. 'I wish I hadn't, though,' she added, slipping it back into the wallet and holding the leather case closed.

'Why? What's happened? You're acting a little strangely,' Gray observed, taking a few cautious steps into the room, the better to see her.

She laughed unevenly, but responded with a question of her own. 'Do you think it was wise to go off and leave me alone like that?'

As if he had somehow been expecting it, he made the logical conclusion instantly. 'You've remembered.'

Rising, Shelby walked over to him and held out the wallet, her eyes never leaving his. 'Everything,' she confirmed pointedly.

Gray frowned faintly, not quite following. 'Surely that's a good thing? You wanted to remember.'

She shrugged. 'I did, until I discovered it was a curate's egg. Only good in parts.'

His frown faded and was replaced by an encouraging smile. 'It was bound to be a shock, sweetheart,' he began, reaching out to take her by the shoulders and offer comfort.

Shelby took a swift step backwards, shrugging him off. 'Don't touch me!' she ordered, and Gray allowed his hands to fall to his sides again.

'What's the problem?' he asked bluntly, visibly drawing himself up ready to respond to whatever she said next.

''What's the problem?'' she parroted with a scornful laugh. 'The problem, darling, is you!'

He folded his arms over the chest she had fallen asleep

on any number of times these past few days, and it speared her heart to recall it.

'Spit it out, Red. Let's hear it,' he commanded tautly, and suddenly the atmosphere in the room could be cut with a knife.

'I understand that you were only doing your job,' Shelby replied, pacing away to the window, then turning to face him, hands rubbing up and down her arms in her agitation. 'Faced with the fact of my accident, you had to do something,' she accepted in a scratchy voice. 'Some lies were inevitable, but did you really have to go so far as to tell me you loved me?' There, it was out, the lie that hurt her to her core. The lie she would never forgive him for.

Gray responded by closing the gap between them, eyes burning into her. 'What makes you think I don't?'

Her own eyes flashed angry sparks at him. 'Because I'm not a fool. It was all a lie. All part of the act that would keep me docile until my memory returned!'

His head went back, as if her words had struck a physical blow, then his nostrils flared as he took in a steadying breath. 'And if I tell you you're wrong?' he countered hardily, and she laughed harshly.

'I wouldn't believe you. You lied to me, Gray, and I'll never forgive you!' she declared passionately, her chin wobbling disastrously.

'No,' Gray argued with a shake of his head. 'Let's get this straight. It isn't the supposed lie you won't forgive, is it? It's that I know you love me. Or are you going to tell me that was a lie too?' he countered tensely.

Her breath hitched in her throat at his insight, and she stared at him. She wanted to say it, to salve her pride, but couldn't. 'It wasn't a lie,' she gritted out through her teeth. 'You were the one who lied. How could you?' She began her nervy pacing again.

The accusation made his jaw clench. 'How could I lie?

By saying we were a couple to protect you from some madman—easily! How could I love you? God knows, right now I don't know how I could, but I do!' he declared in a raised voice that halted her in her tracks.

'Stop saying that,' Shelby ordered, feeling confused and shaken. This wasn't at all the way she had expected him to react to her having discovered the truth. He was the one in the wrong—wasn't he? He was the one who had lied, so why was he acting so hurt and outraged? He ought to be apologising to her, trying to explain his actions.

Gray propped himself against the nearby wardrobe and folded his arms, looking prepared to stay there for ever. 'No. I can't take it back, and wouldn't if I could. You want the truth and so do I. I'm tired of having to pretend I don't care. When I told you I loved you, it was the honest truth. I love you, Shelby. What are you going to do about it?'

That struck a nerve with her. 'What do you know about pretending you don't care?' she charged scornfully, and his brows rose mockingly.

'What? You think you have a monopoly on hiding your feelings? Dream on, Red. I fell in love with you when you were eighteen years old!' he informed her in a tone that was way short of lover-like.

Shelby's lips parted on a sharp intake of breath. 'You couldn't have,' she protested, for that was when she had fallen in love with him.

He smiled grimly. 'Couldn't I? You have no idea. I held out my hand to help you out of a taxi, like I'd done count-less times before, but this was different. You looked up at me with those big green eyes of yours, and I fell head over heels,' he confessed, shaking his head at the memory. 'I spent the next ten years hiding the fact.'

She was totally stunned. If he was to be believed, they had fallen in love with each other at the same moment. It was incredible. She had told nobody, not even her father, so there was no way Gray could know the how of it from her or any other source. Which meant everything he had just told her had to be his truth. If that was so, then it would mean he hadn't lied. Her hand rose to her mouth and she stared at him over it, her eyes huge with wonder and uncertainty.

'That was when I fell in love with you,' she told him in an awestruck voice, all the anger draining out of her in the face of his confession.

At her words it was Gray's turn to be dumbfounded. He straightened up abruptly. 'What? You're kidding?' he challenged in disbelief.

Shelby shook her head. 'No. You took my hand, and…' She allowed the rest to tail off. He would make his own connection.

Gray took a deep breath, then dragged a very shaky hand through his hair. 'You know what this means, don't you? We've loved each other for ten years and hid it so well that neither of us even guessed! If you believe I really do love you, that is?' He looked a question that made her wince.

'Yes, I believe you. There's no way you could have made that up,' she told him honestly. 'Like you, I worked so hard not to give myself away. When I thought I had, because of your lie, I struck out. I'm sorry.'

Gray allowed himself a faint smile. 'You were hurt. It's understandable.'

'How can you forgive me so easily?' she just had to ask, and his smile softened.

'Because I love you, Red. It's as simple as that,' he told her, and this time when he went to take her in his arms she didn't pull away. 'For the record, I hated having to lie to you. Unfortunately it was necessary.'

Shelby slipped her arms around him and held on tight. From the depths of despair just moments ago, she was discovering happiness was within her grasp again. 'I understand now. It was just such a shock—remembering that way. That picture…' She fell silent for a moment, recalling other things. 'You kept the photograph?' She frowned up at him and his lips twitched.

'You looked beautiful in it.'

Her heart did a tiny skip. 'And the handkerchief?'

'It was my way of holding on to your kiss,' he told her simply and brought tears to her eyes.

'I think that's the most romantic thing I've ever heard!' Shelby exclaimed, her heart swelling with love for him.

Gray looked at her seriously. 'You're very precious to me, Red,' he told her in a husky voice. 'When Oscar told me about the threats, I couldn't get back to you fast enough. When you refused to take it seriously, I wanted to throttle you. If you had died, my life would have been over. That was when I decided I had to partly show my hand. I couldn't face losing you, so I had to find out if there was ever going to be anything between us. When I realised you wanted me as much as I wanted you, I decided to go for it. If a love affair was all it would turn out to be, hell, at least I would have had that.'

A tiny laugh escaped her. 'We're too much alike. I was thinking the same thing.'

He groaned a wry acknowledgement. 'So, here we were, supposed lovers, with me knowing we weren't and you fully expecting us to be sharing a bed. You pushed my resolve to its very limits. I don't know how long I could have held out if I hadn't got that phone call from your father.'

Shelby leaned back slightly so she could see his face. 'Of course. Now I get it. I didn't understand. I thought you'd given in to the inevitable. Dad gave you the all-clear, didn't he, and that meant I was no longer off limits. That's why you made love to me!'

Gray dropped his forehead down to rest on hers. 'Thank

God for that call. I was going out of my mind. Another night like that one and I wouldn't have been accountable!'

Laughter bubbled out of her at that. 'And there I was doing my best to seduce you. But you could have made love to me, Gray. I wanted you to, and I didn't remember we hadn't actually got that far.'

'Which only added to my torment,' he admitted dryly. 'But I couldn't have made love to you, Red, for the very reason you pointed out. You didn't know what was a lie.'

'Yet we did make love,' she reminded him, and he sighed.

'True. After which I told you I loved you. I hoped the truth of that would outweigh the lie in the end.'

She recalled something else. 'You told me to remember you loved me. I didn't know why, but I understand now. It was because you feared something like this happening, wasn't it?'

Gray pulled her back into his arms and rested his chin on her hair. 'When I told you I loved you, I didn't expect you to tell me you loved me back. Hoped for it, but didn't expect it. When you told me, I realised that your lack of memory had made you vulnerable to the truth when you finally remembered it. I hoped that my words would soften the blow.'

Shelby sighed wistfully. 'It would have done if I'd remembered what you said. I do love you, Gray. So much that I can't put it into words. When I think of all the time I wasted, going out with those other men. Pretending I was having a grand old time, when really I was pining for you.'

'That makes two of us, darling,' Gray confessed. 'Those women were for show. The only one I wanted was you. I think your father guessed I had a soft spot for you. That was why he told me that being faint hearted wouldn't get me what I wanted.'

A light went on in Shelby's brain. 'I think you're right.

When we were at the airport on our way here, I let slip to him that I loved you. He must have realised that the pair of us were hopeless cases and decided to do a little match-making of his own!'

Gray's laugh was wonderfully light-hearted. 'Thank goodness he did.'

'You know he's going to think he engineered the whole thing, don't you? We're never going to live it down.'

'He'll tell the children too,' Gray added with a laugh.

'Whose children?' Shelby asked, heart tripping as she looked up at him.

Blue eyes smiled down at her. 'Ours, of course. Providing you marry me.'

Happiness was a huge bubble inside her. 'Are you asking me to marry you?' she teased lightly, never having any intention of saying anything other than yes.

'You're the only woman I ever intend to marry, so yes, I'm asking. Will you marry me, Red?' he asked solemnly, and her love for him overflowed.

'Oh, yes. A thousand times yes,' she accepted, reaching up to kiss him.

Gray kissed her back, and for a moment the world outside stopped existing as they sealed their vow. Then he broke the kiss and swept her up in his arms, carrying her over to the freshly made bed. There was a wealth of love and laughter in his eyes as he laid her down and joined her.

'We'll do the shopping later. Right now I have an urgent need to make love with you.'

'Now that sounds like a plan,' she sighed, then frowned. 'Talking of plans, you never did tell me what plan C was,' she reminded him, and Gray grinned that wonderfully se-ductive wolfish grin of his.

'Plan C, darling, was to get you to fall in love with me,'

he informed her ironically. 'It's now redundant, I'm happy to say.'

Her fingers found their way into his hair and teased the silky strands. 'Hmm, I'm so glad I have you at last.' She sighed happily.

'You've always had me, Red. From the moment I set eyes on you getting out of that taxi, I was hooked,' he admitted without a trace of regret. 'I only agreed to help your father that time because the man was bad news and I wanted you for myself. I intended to woo you and ask you to marry me then, but Oscar's confession got in the way and I was forced to retrench. I didn't know how long I would have to wait to try again. Do you forgive me for lying to you? I had the best intentions.'

'I was wrong not to let you explain, and I've regretted that. Of course I forgive you. I love you; what else can I do? Let's put the past where it belongs. We've a lot of time to make up for,' Shelby pointed out, reaching for the hem of his T-shirt, and he laughed. 'What's so funny?'

'You told me once I'd never find out how passionate you are in bed,' he reminded her, and she grinned.

'You shouldn't have said that. Now I'm going to have to make you pay for it,' she threatened.

Gray lay back with a husky laugh. 'I was hoping you were going to say that.'

MILLS & BOON®

Live the emotion

Royal Proposals

Romantic, passionate, glamorous — it's how the other half loves!

In March 2006, By Request brings back three favourite romances by our bestselling Mills & Boon authors:

The Prince's Pleasure by Robyn Donald
A Royal Proposition by Marion Lennox
The Sheikh's Proposal by Barbara McMahon

Make sure you buy these irresistible stories!

On sale 3rd March 2006

Available at WHSmith, Tesco, ASDA, Borders, Eason, Sainsbury's and most bookshops

www.millsandboon.co.uk

FREE

4 BOOKS AND A SURPRISE GIFT!

We would like to take this opportunity to thank you for reading this Mills & Boon® book by offering you the chance to take FOUR more specially selected titles from the Modern Romance™ series absolutely FREE! We're also making this offer to introduce you to the benefits of the Reader Service™—

- ★ **FREE home delivery**
- ★ **FREE gifts and competitions**
- ★ **FREE monthly Newsletter**
- ★ **Books available before they're in the shops**
- ★ **Exclusive Reader Service offers**

Accepting these FREE books and gift places you under no obligation to buy; you may cancel at any time, even after receiving your free shipment. Simply complete your details below and return the entire page to the address below. You don't even need a stamp!

YES! Please send me 4 free Modern Romance books and a surprise gift. I understand that unless you hear from me, I will receive 6 superb new titles every month for just £2.75 each, postage and packing free. I am under no obligation to purchase any books and may cancel my subscription at any time. The free books and gift will be mine to keep in any case.

P6ZEE

Ms/Mrs/Miss/Mr.....................................Initials ....
BLOCK CAPITALS PLEASE

Surname ....

Address ....

....

....Postcode ....

Send this whole page to:
The Reader Service, FREEPOST CN81, Croydon, CR9 3WZ